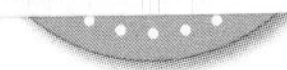

Common Core

Standards for Mathematical Content

Domain Measurement and Data

Cluster Solve problems involving measurement and estimation of intervals of time, liquid volumes, and masses of objects.

Standard 3.MD.1

Standards for Mathematical Practice

- ✔ Make sense of problems and persevere in solving them.
- ✔ Reason abstractly and quantitatively.
- ✔ Construct viable arguments and critique the reasoning of others.
- ✔ Model with mathematics.
- ✔ Use appropriate tools strategically.
- ✔ Attend to precision.
- ✔ Look for and make use of structure.
- ✔ Look for and express regularity in repeated reasoning.

Time

Planning

Lessons

Review and Assessment

ISBN-13: 978-0-328-67382-7
ISBN-10: 0-328-67382-X

10 V064 15 14 13

Topic 12 Time

MATH BACKGROUND

BIG IDEA Measurement Some attributes of objects are measurable and can be quantified using unit amounts.

ESSENTIAL UNDERSTANDINGS

12-1 Time can be expressed using different units that are related to each other.

12-2 The minute hand takes 5 minutes to move from one number to the next on a typical clock face. The minute hand takes 1 minute to move from one mark to the next on a typical clock face.

12-3 There are different units for measuring time. Many clock times can be expressed in more than one way.

12-4 The duration of an event can be measured if one knows the start and end times for the event.

BIG IDEA Practices, Processes, and Proficiencies Mathematics content and practices can be applied to solve problems.

ESSENTIAL UNDERSTANDING

12-5 Some problems with the initial data point unknown can be solved by starting with the end result, reversing the steps and processes, and working backward to the initial data point.

Time Concepts

Time is the duration of an event from beginning to end. Time can be measured in standard units such as seconds, minutes, hours, and days. Time can also be measured in any nonstandard unit that repeats predictably, such as a metronome or pendulum swing.

This topic focuses on how to read analog and digital clocks to the nearest half hour, quarter hour, and minute. Students also learn how to use the context of a real-life situation to determine whether a time should be designated as A.M. or P.M.

Time and Fractions

The terms *half hour* and *quarter hour* can be understood by considering an analog clock face as a circle and dividing it into fractional parts.

The sweep of the minute hand from 12 to 6 demonstrates the division of the hour into halves.

There are 2 groups of 30 minutes in each hour.

There are 6 groups of 5 minutes in each half hour.

The sweep of the minute hand from 12 to 3 demonstrates the division of the hour into quarters.

There are 4 groups of 15 minutes in each hour.

There are 3 groups of 5 minutes in each quarter hour.

Mathematical Practices: Use Structure

Remind students that they already know how to count by 5s and add on 1s. Emphasize the use of these skills when learning about time.

Reading an Analog Clock

Reading time on an analog clock requires an understanding of the movement of the hands. Students must remember that clock hands do not move at the same speed. The minute hand moves 12 times as fast as the hour hand. So, for instance, as the time progresses from 5:00 to 5:15, the minute hand moves one fourth of the way around the clock, but the hour hand moves only one fourth of the distance from 5 to 6. This is illustrated in the figure below.

Mathematical Practices: Reason Quantitatively

Prior to teaching students how to tell time, you may want to review skip counting skills with them. Skip count by 5s and 10s and explain that this will be helpful when reading the minutes on the clock. If some students are not familiar with the parts of an analog clock, you may want to review the hour hand, minute hand, and even second hand.

Analog Versus Digital Clocks

Analog and digital clocks have distinct advantages and disadvantages. Digital clocks show a numeric display of the time, and so they provide a numeric means of calculating the passage of time. For instance, the digital clocks pictured below record the same times as the analog clocks shown to the left.

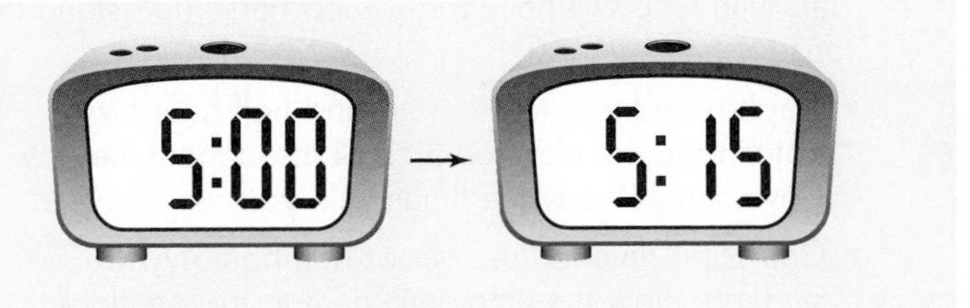

With the digital clock, a simple mental subtraction leads to the conclusion that 15 minutes have passed. But the analog clock, although more difficult to read, actually conveys the concept of the passage of 15 minutes in that the movement of the hands is visible.

Using an analog clock to develop a sense of the passage of time actually helps in reading a digital clock. When reading a digital clock that says 7:56, for instance, the idea of the analog clock helps in understanding that this time means "almost 8 o'clock."

For a complete list of *enVisionMATH* Professional Development resources in print, on DVD, and online, see the *Teacher's Program Overview.*

DIFFERENTIATED INSTRUCTION

ELL

Considerations for ELL Students

Repeated oral language practice of the terms that are used with time will help English learners understand the concepts.

- Emphasize times to the hour and half hour by pointing to the classroom clock throughout the day. Have students say the times with you.
- Call out a time to the hour or half hour. Have students show the time on a demonstration clock.
- Place both clock hands at 12 on a demonstration clock. Move the minute hand to each number and count by 5s as students count along with you.

Special Needs

Considerations for Special Needs Students

- Display digital and analog clocks that show the same time. Have students say the times in different ways.
- Set an alarm clock for a certain time. When the clock rings, have students say the times aloud in different ways.

Below Level

Considerations for Below-Level Students

- Make sure students understand the different parts of an analog clock. These include the hour and minute hand, marks for minutes, and hour numbers. Review and explain the differences between the hour and minute hands of the clock and what their purpose is. Ask students to explain what each mark for minutes on the clock means.
- Some students may confuse the numbers on an analog clock with the number of minutes that have passed. Explain that when the minute hand moves from one minute mark to the next, one minute has passed. You may want to discuss activities that last for one minute compared to activities that last for one hour.

Advanced/Gifted

Considerations for Advanced/Gifted Students

- At different times during the day, point to the clock and have students say the times in different ways, including times to the minute.
- Challenge students to write descriptions of what they do at certain times of the day.

Response to Intervention

Ongoing Intervention

- Lessons with guiding questions to assess understanding
- Support to prevent misconceptions and to reteach

TIER 2
STRATEGIC

Strategic Intervention

- Targeted to small groups who need more support
- Easy to implement

Intensive Intervention

- Instruction to accelerate progress
- Instruction focused on foundational skills

Reading Comprehension and Problem Solving

Use Structure: Use Reading Comprehension Strategies

Some students can read a word problem (decode the words) but need help determining important ideas and drawing conclusions from the text.

Questions to Guide Comprehension

Use questions like those here to guide comprehension. (Use prior knowledge; represent text information in different ways.)

From Lesson 12-2 Exercise 9

The Hubble Space Telescope has been moving in its orbit for 1 hour. In 37 more minutes it will complete an orbit. How many minutes does it take the Hubble Space Telescope to complete 1 orbit?

1 *What question do you need to answer?*
[How many minutes does it take the Hubble Space Telescope to complete 1 orbit?]

2 *What important information is needed to answer the question?*
[The Hubble Space Telescope has been moving in its orbit for 1 hour and in 37 minutes it will complete an orbit.]

3 *What other important information do you need to know to answer the question?*
[I need to know that 1 hour = 60 minutes.]

4 *How can you represent the important information in a drawing?*
[I can draw a line segment to stand for 1 orbit and make a bar of the same length that has two sections. One section is labeled 1 hour, and the other is labeled 37 minutes.]

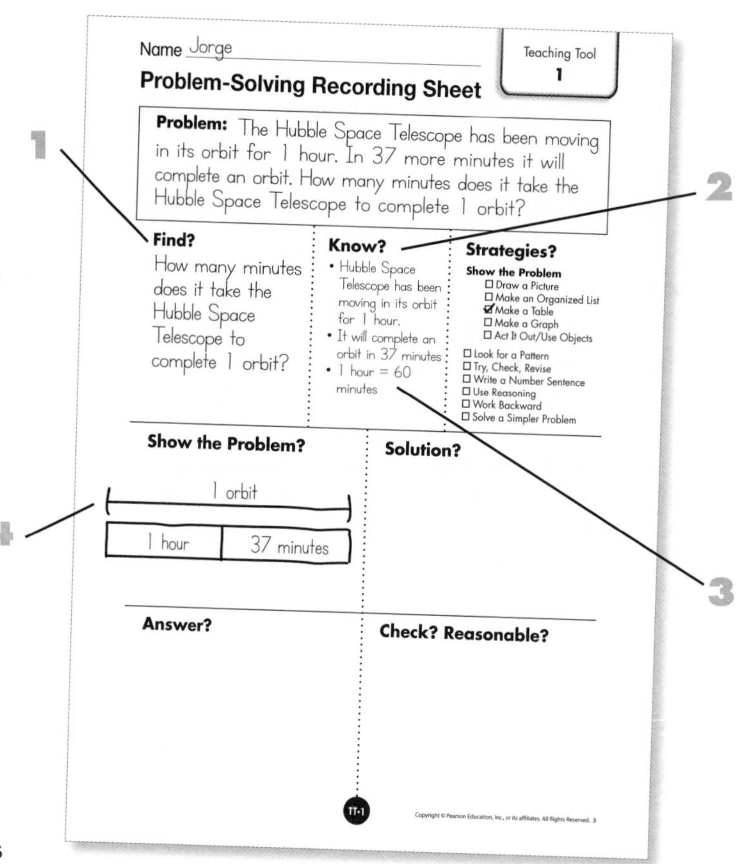
Name Jorge

Teaching Tool 1

Problem-Solving Recording Sheet

Problem: The Hubble Space Telescope has been moving in its orbit for 1 hour. In 37 more minutes it will complete an orbit. How many minutes does it take the Hubble Space Telescope to complete 1 orbit?

Find?
How many minutes does it take the Hubble Space Telescope to complete 1 orbit?

Know?
- Hubble Space Telescope has been moving in its orbit for 1 hour.
- It will complete an orbit in 37 minutes
- 1 hour = 60 minutes

Strategies?
Show the Problem
☐ Draw a Picture
☐ Make an Organized List
☑ Make a Table
☐ Make a Graph
☐ Act It Out/Use Objects
☐ Look for a Pattern
☐ Try, Check, Revise
☐ Write a Number Sentence
☐ Use Reasoning
☐ Work Backward
☐ Solve a Simpler Problem

Show the Problem?
1 orbit
1 hour | 37 minutes

Solution?

Answer?

Check? Reasonable?

TT-1

Vocabulary Activities

Daily Schedule

Attend to Precision Have students make a two-column chart and label the left column "Time" and the right column "Activity." Then have them fill the left column with the times they start ten different activities on an average school day (be sure students note "A.M." or "P.M.") In the right column, have students note the activity. Underneath the completed lists, have students complete the following sentence frames: *I begin [number] activities on the hour. I begin [number] activities on the half hour. I begin [number] activities on the quarter hour.*

Time	Activity
7:15 A.M.	Wake up
8:00 A.M.	Leave for school
9:30 A.M.	Math class
12:15 P.M.	Eat lunch
12:30 P.M.	Play outside
3:00 P.M.	Leave school
4:30 P.M.	Start homework
5:30 P.M.	Eat dinner
8:00 P.M.	Shower
8:30 P.M.	Go to bed

Math and Literature

WorldScapes Readers™

WorldScapes
Below Zero
Written by Claire Owen

Below Zero For activity suggestions for pp. 14–15 of *Below Zero*, see *Guided Problem Solving for the Math Library.*

TOPIC OPENER

Math Project

Social Studies

Factoid

In 1965, the rockfish became Maryland's official state fish. The rockfish is also called striped bass, and is known for its size and fighting ability. With hundreds of species of fish to catch, recreational fishing is very popular in Maryland. Some people charter a fishing boat. This gives them access to a boat, equipment, and a professional guide for a specified amount of time.

Directions

Have students work in small groups. Tell them that each group owns three charter fishing boats. One boat takes 3-hour trips, another boat takes $5\frac{1}{2}$-hour trips, and the third boat takes 8-hour trips. Ask each group to name its three boats. Then have them write the name of each boat, the length of its trip, and possible starting and ending times for the trip.

BIG CATCH
3 hours
Start 7:00 A.M.
End 10:00 A.M.

FUN AND SUN
$5\frac{1}{2}$ hours
Start 10:00 A.M.
End 3:30 P.M.

ATLANTIC WAVES
8 hours
Start 8:00 A.M.
End: 4:00 P.M.

Home-School Connection

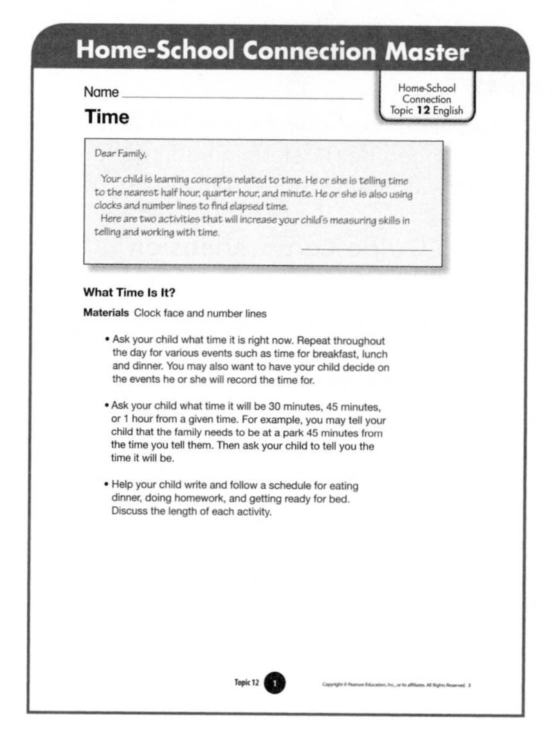

Home-School Connection Master

Name ____________

Home-School Connection Topic **12** English

Time

Dear Family,

Your child is learning concepts related to time. He or she is telling time to the nearest half hour, quarter hour, and minute. He or she is also using clocks and number lines to find elapsed time.

Here are two activities that will increase your child's measuring skills in telling and working with time.

What Time Is It?

Materials Clock face and number lines

- Ask your child what time it is right now. Repeat throughout the day for various events such as time for breakfast, lunch and dinner. You may also want to have your child decide on the events he or she will record the time for.
- Ask your child what time it will be 30 minutes, 45 minutes, or 1 hour from a given time. For example, you may tell your child that the family needs to be at a park 45 minutes from the time you tell them. Then ask your child to tell you the time it will be.
- Help your child write and follow a schedule for eating dinner, doing homework, and getting ready for bed. Discuss the length of each activity.

Purpose

Provide families with a quick overview of the content that will be taught in Topic 12. Read the Dear Family letter to the students and have them sign it. Also available in Spanish.

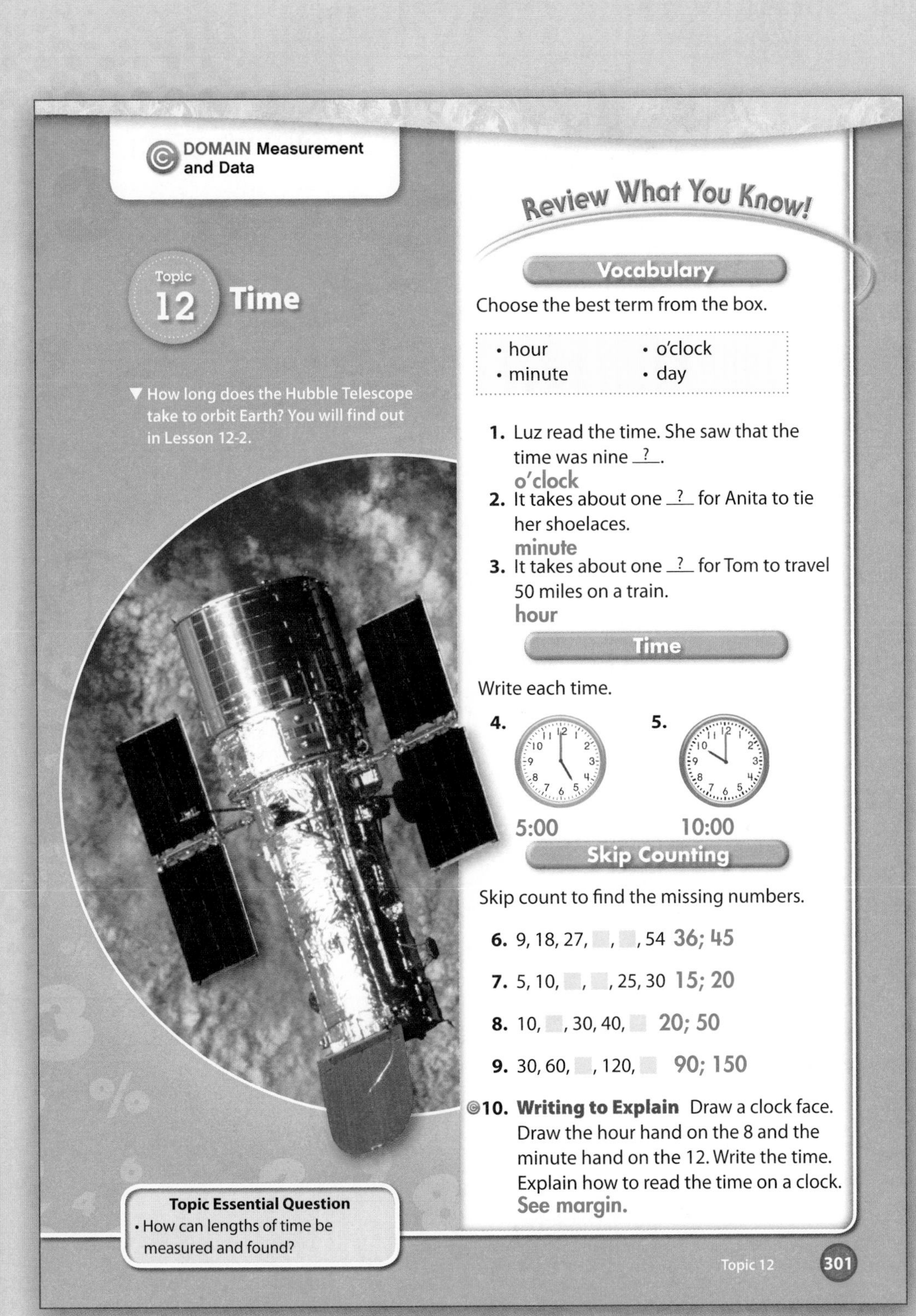

DOMAIN Measurement and Data

Topic 12 **Time**

▼ How long does the Hubble Telescope take to orbit Earth? You will find out in Lesson 12-2.

Topic Essential Question
• How can lengths of time be measured and found?

Review What You Know!

Vocabulary

Choose the best term from the box.

• hour • o'clock
• minute • day

1. Luz read the time. She saw that the time was nine _?_. **o'clock**
2. It takes about one _?_ for Anita to tie her shoelaces. **minute**
3. It takes about one _?_ for Tom to travel 50 miles on a train. **hour**

Time

Write each time.

4. **5:00**
5. **10:00**

Skip Counting

Skip count to find the missing numbers.

6. 9, 18, 27, ▢, ▢, 54 **36; 45**
7. 5, 10, ▢, ▢, 25, 30 **15; 20**
8. 10, ▢, 30, 40, ▢ **20; 50**
9. 30, 60, ▢, 120, ▢ **90; 150**
10. **Writing to Explain** Draw a clock face. Draw the hour hand on the 8 and the minute hand on the 12. Write the time. Explain how to read the time on a clock. **See margin.**

Topic 12 301

Topic Essential Question

• How can lengths of time be measured and found?

Revisit the question throughout the topic. Students will be able to answer the Topic Essential Question by the end of the topic.

New Vocabulary

hour
half hour
quarter hour
minute
seconds
A.M.
P.M.
elapsed time

half hour

Cards can always be used as flash cards and for playing a matching game. Another option is to display a clock face with the hands set to 3:00. Hold up the *half hour* card and have a volunteer show the time a half hour later and then a half hour before. Repeat with the *quarter hour* card.

Review What You Know!

Purpose

Assign each set of exercises and go over the answers with students.

10. Check that students draw a clock face showing 8:00. Sample answer: Find the number that the hour hand points to. It points to 8. Find the number that the minute hand points to. It points to 12. The time is 8 o'clock or 8:00.

Topic 12 Time

INTERACTIVE LEARNING

For full teacher support of each Problem-Based Interactive Learning activity, see the **Develop the Concept: Interactive** page of each lesson in the Topic 12 Teacher's Edition.

Lesson 12-1 Time to the Half Hour and Quarter Hour

Purpose To understand that time can be measured in half hours and quarter hours (quarter after and quarter to)

Mathematical Practices

- Use Appropriate Tools
- Attend to Precision
- Reason Quantitatively
- Make Generalizations

Lesson 12-2 Time to the Minute

Purpose To understand that time can be measured to the minute and read on the clock by skip counting by 5s and 10s

Mathematical Practices

- Attend to Precision
- Use Appropriate Tools
- Reason Quantitatively
- Make Generalizations

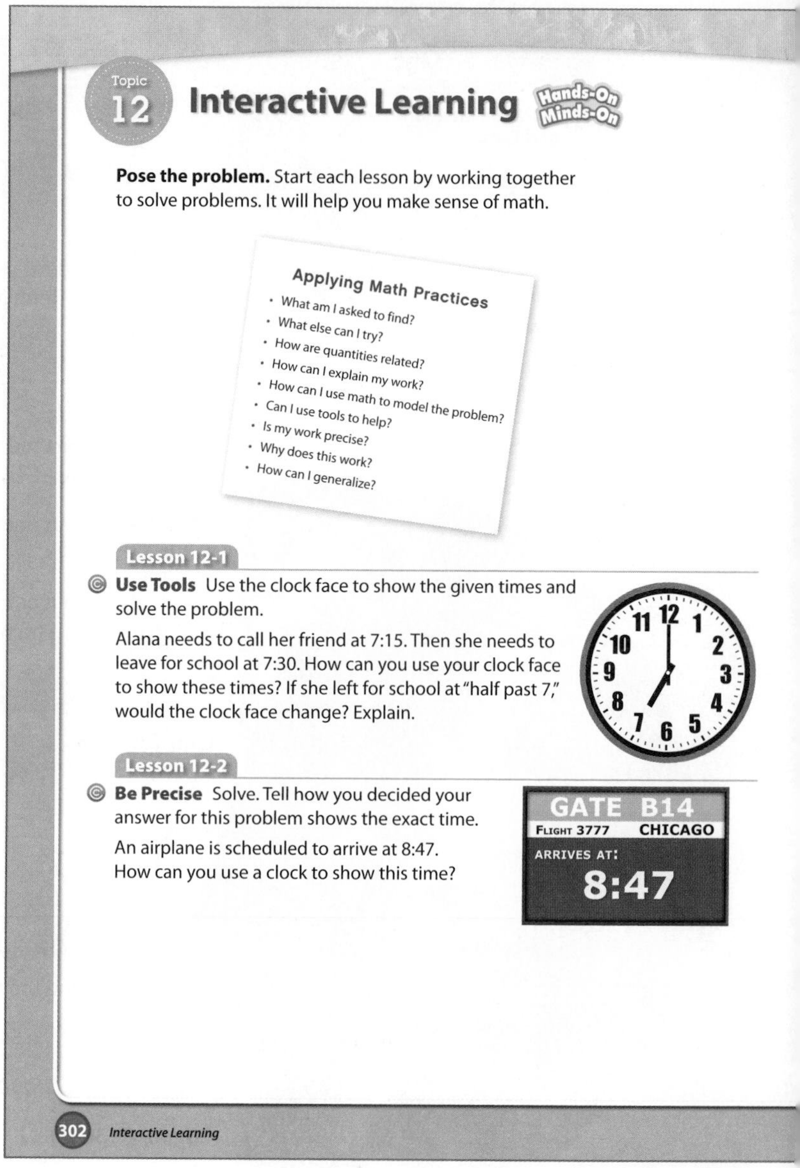

Interactive Learning

Pose the problem. Start each lesson by working together to solve problems. It will help you make sense of math.

Applying Math Practices

- What am I asked to find?
- What else can I try?
- How are quantities related?
- How can I explain my work?
- How can I use math to model the problem?
- Can I use tools to help?
- Is my work precise?
- Why does this work?
- How can I generalize?

Lesson 12-1

Use Tools Use the clock face to show the given times and solve the problem.

Alana needs to call her friend at 7:15. Then she needs to leave for school at 7:30. How can you use your clock face to show these times? If she left for school at "half past 7," would the clock face change? Explain.

Lesson 12-2

Be Precise Solve. Tell how you decided your answer for this problem shows the exact time.

An airplane is scheduled to arrive at 8:47. How can you use a clock to show this time?

Interactive Learning

MATHEMATICAL PRACTICES

Lesson 12-3

Generalize Solve. Tell how you decided.

A class is going to collect newspapers as part of a recycling project. They will collect newspapers for 3 weeks. How many days are in 3 weeks?

APRIL

S	M	T	W	T	F	S
			1	2	3	4
5	6	7	8	9	10	11
12	13	14	15	16	17	18
19	20	21	22	23	24	25
26	27	28	29	30		

Lesson 12-4

Use Tools Solve any way you choose. Use a clock face to help.

Denise went to see a movie. The movie started at 1:00 P.M. It ended at 2:35 P.M. How long did the movie last?

Lesson 12-5

Model Solve any way you choose. Use a clock face to help.

Nina wants to arrive at the community center at 9:30 A.M. for an art class. It takes her 15 minutes to walk to the center, 15 minutes to get ready, and 30 minutes to make and eat breakfast. What time should she start making breakfast?

Arrive at Community Center

Lesson 12-3 **Units of Time**

Purpose To understand that there are relationships that make it possible to change between any two units of time

Mathematical Practices

- Make Generalizations
- Attend to Precision
- Use Appropriate Tools
- Reason Quantitatively

Lesson 12-4 **Elapsed Time**

Purpose To understand that elapsed time tells how long something lasts

Mathematical Practices

- Use Appropriate Tools
- Persevere in Solving Problems
- Attend to Precision
- Model with Mathematics
- Reason Quantitatively

Lesson 12-5 **Problem Solving: Work Backward**

Purpose To understand that starting with the end result and working backward step-by-step to the beginning will help solve some problems

Mathematical Practices

- Model with Mathematics
- Persevere in Solving Problems
- Attend to Precision
- Use Appropriate Tools
- Reason Quantitatively

Lesson

12-1

Common Core

Domain

Measurement and Data

Cluster

Solve problems involving measurement and estimation of intervals of time, liquid volumes, and masses of objects.

Standard

3.MD.1 Tell and write time to the nearest minute and measure time intervals in minutes. Solve word problems involving addition and subtraction of time intervals in minutes, e.g., by representing the problem on a number line diagram.

Mathematical Practices

- ○ Make sense of problems and persevere in solving them.
- ✔ Reason abstractly and quantitatively.
- ✔ Construct viable arguments and critique the reasoning of others.
- ✔ Model with mathematics.
- ✔ Use appropriate tools strategically.
- ○ Attend to precision.
- ✔ Look for and make use of structure.
- ○ Look for and express regularity in repeated reasoning.

Time to the Half Hour and Quarter Hour

Lesson Overview

Objective	Essential Understanding	Vocabulary	Materials
Students will tell time to the nearest half hour and quarter hour using analog and digital clocks, and identify times as A.M. or P.M.	Time can be expressed using different units that are related to each other. A.M. and P.M. are used to designate certain time periods.	**hour** **half hour** **quarter hour** **minute** **seconds** **A.M.** **P.M.**	Clock face (Teaching Tool 25)

Math Background

Research says ... 5-year-olds equate time, speed, and distance with the relative stopping points of moving objects (Richards & Siegler, 1979). Many children master both the speed and distance concepts by age 8 and the majority master both by age 11.

The time concept appears to be mastered sometime between age 11 and adulthood. Students require many types of experiences with time concepts. In the lessons that follow, students will have an opportunity to tell time and measure time in different units.

Some students may ask what A.M. and P.M. stand for. A.M. is an abbreviation of the Latin term *ante meridiem*, which means "before midday," or "before noon." P.M. is an abbreviation of *post meridiem*, which means "after midday," or "after noon."

1 Daily Common Core Review

Daily Common Core Review

Name ______________

Daily Common Core Review **12-1**

Choose the best answer.

1. Karen's score on a computer game is 321 points. Greg's score is 244 points. How many more points does Karen have than Greg?
   - A 76
   - (B) 77
   - C 78
   - D 87

2. Ben cut his peanut butter and jelly sandwich into four equal pieces. He ate one piece. What is the fraction of the sandwich that Ben ate?
   - A $\frac{3}{4}$
   - B $\frac{1}{2}$
   - (C) $\frac{1}{4}$
   - D $\frac{1}{8}$

3. Each tile on Ms. Engle's kitchen floor has 6 sides. What is the name of this polygon?
   - A Pentagon
   - (B) Hexagon
   - C Heptagon
   - D Octagon

4. **Estimation** Which is the best estimate for the length of a table?
   - A 6 inches
   - B 6 miles
   - C 6 yards
   - (D) 6 feet

5. There are 3 lines of people waiting to enter a museum. Each line has 12 people. How many people are in line all together?
   36

6. What symbol makes this sentence true? Use <, >, or =.
   571 (>) 549

7. What fraction of the figure is shaded?
   $\frac{5}{8}$

8. What is 903 − 457?
   446

D 12-1

Also available in print

Content Reviewed

Exercise 1	Subtraction with Whole Numbers
Exercise 2	Fraction Concepts
Exercise 3	Geometry
Exercise 4	Measurement/Estimation
Exercise 5	Multiplication
Exercise 6	Compare Whole Numbers
Exercise 7	Identify Fractions
Exercise 8	Subtraction

2 Develop the Concept: Interactive

10–15 min

Problem-Based Interactive Learning

Overview Students will show and tell time to the half hour and quarter hour on pupil clock faces.

Focus How do you tell time to the nearest quarter hour or half hour?

Materials Pupil's clock face (1 per group), blank clock faces (Teaching Tool 25)

Set the Purpose *You know how to tell time to the hour. You also know how to count by 1s and by 5s. Today, you will use these skills to help tell other times on a clock.*

Connect *In your daily life, when is reading a clock or giving a time important?* [Sample answers: following a schedule; meeting someone; getting to practice on time]

MATHEMATICAL PRACTICES

Use Appropriate Tools Tell students to use the position of the hour and minute hand to help them tell time.

Pose the Problem *Alana needs to call her friend at 7:15. Then she needs to leave for school at 7:30. How can you use your clock face to show these times so she will be on time?* Have students work in pairs to show 7:15 and 7:30 on their clock faces. Ask volunteers to explain how they decided where to put the minute hand and hour hand.

Whole-Class Discussion *Where is the minute hand at 7:15?* [On 3] *Where is the hour hand?* [A little past 7] *Fifteen minutes is a quarter hour. Why?* [3 is one quarter of the way around the clock.] On the board write the digital time and how the time is said. [7:15 or quarter past 7]. *Where is the minute hand at 7:30?* [On 6] *Where is the hour hand?* [Halfway between 7 and 8]. *Thirty minutes is a half hour. If the 12 shows the beginning of the hour, what does the 6 represent? Why?* [A half hour because the six is halfway around the clock] On the board write the digital time and how the time is said. [7:30; half past 7]. Show 7:45 on the board and ask students to show this time on their clock faces. *What time is shown?* [7:45] *How many minutes is it before 8:00?* [15] *What might another name be for this time that uses fractions?* [quarter to 8]

Small-Group Interaction Distribute a copy of Teaching Tool 25 to each student. *Partner 1 says a time—quarter past or half past the hour. Partner 2 draws the hands, and writes the time in two ways (digital and words). Then partners switch roles.*

List different events that could happen at a time such as 7:30. Write A.M. for morning and P.M. for afternoon and evening.

3 Develop the Concept: Visual

Visual Learning

Time to the Half Hour and Quarter Hour

How do you tell time to the nearest half hour or quarter hour?

The clocks show the time that the bus arrives at school and the time it leaves.

Units of Time
1 day = 24 hours
1 hour = 60 minutes
1 half hour = 30 minutes
1 quarter hour = 15 minutes
1 minute = 60 seconds

Bus Arrives 8:30

Bus Leaves 2:45

Look at the pictures of the clock faces. Where does the minute hand point on each clock? [To the 6; to the 9] *What do the 6 and 9 represent?* [30 minutes and 45 minutes] *How are the minutes different?* [They are 15 minutes apart.]

Tell the time the bus arrives.

Write 8:30 in three other ways.

When the minute hand is on the 6, you can say the time is "half past" the hour.

The bus arrives at *eight thirty*, or *half past eight*, or *30 minutes past eight*.

1 Visual Learning

Set the Purpose Call students' attention to the **Visual Learning Bridge** at the top of the page. *In this lesson you will learn to tell time to the nearest half hour or quarter hour and how to use reasoning to determine whether to use A.M. or P.M. after a given time.*

Animated Glossary Students can see highlighted words defined in the Online Student Edition.
hour, half hour, quarter hour, minute, seconds, A.M., P.M.
www.pearsonsuccessnet.com

Another Example

Which word or words in the first problem tell whether the time was in the morning or evening? [The words "arrives at"; the time has to be in the morning because that's when the bus arrives at school.] *Which word or words in the second problem tell whether the time was in the morning or evening?* [The word "leaves"; the time has to be in the afternoon because that's when the bus leaves school.]

Explain It

In Exercise 1, explain to students that sometimes you need to use A.M. or P.M. when you give a time. *Suppose I said that I brush my teeth every day at 7:30. Would I more likely be brushing my teeth at 7:30 A.M. or 7:30 P.M.?* [It could be either time. You might be brushing your teeth in the morning at 7:30 A.M., after you get up, or in the evening at 7:30 P.M., before you go to bed.]

Time to the Half Hour and Quarter Hour

How do you tell time to the nearest half hour or quarter hour?

The clocks show the time that the bus arrives at school and the time it leaves.

Units of Time
1 day = 24 hours
1 hour = 60 minutes
1 half hour = 30 minutes
1 quarter hour = 15 minutes
1 minute = 60 seconds

Bus Arrives

Bus Leaves

Another Example **How do you decide whether the time is A.M. or P.M.?**

The hours of the day between midnight and noon are A.M. hours.
The hours between noon and midnight are P.M. hours.

Would the time the bus arrives at school more likely be 8:30 A.M. or 8:30 P.M.?

8:30 P.M. is in the evening. The bus probably would not arrive at school in the evening. 8:30 A.M. is in the morning.

The bus would more likely arrive at school at 8:30 A.M.

Would the time the bus leaves school more likely be 2:45 A.M. or 2:45 P.M.?

2:45 A.M. is in the middle of the night. The bus probably would not be leaving school at that time. 2:45 P.M. is in the afternoon.

The bus would more likely leave school at 2:45 P.M.

Explain It

1. Why might it be important to use A.M. or P.M. when you give a time? See margin.
2. Would you be more likely to leave your home to go to school at 8:15 A.M. or 8:15 P.M.? See margin.
3. Would you be more likely to eat lunch at 12:30 A.M. or 12:30 P.M.? See margin.

Answers

1. Sample answer: Sometimes it is not clear whether the time given is in the morning or evening.
2. 8:15 A.M.; Since 8:15 P.M. is in the evening, I would not be leaving for school at that time.
3. 12:30 P.M.; Since 12:30 A.M. is just 1 half hour after midnight, I would not be eating lunch at that time.

ELL STRATEGY Visual Learning

Visual Learning Animation

www.pearsonsuccessnet.com or CD

Why do you think the fraction word "half" is used to name the time when the minute hand is on the 6? [Because the minute hand is halfway around the clock]

Tell the time the bus leaves.

Write 2:45 in three other ways.

When the minute hand is on the 9, you can say the time is "15 minutes to" or "quarter to" the hour.

The bus leaves at *two forty-five*, or *15 minutes to three*, or *quarter to three*.

Prevent Misconceptions

Help students who find it difficult to learn the different ways to tell the same time by making a chart to show the different ways.

Times Before the Hour		Times After the Hour	
7:45	quarter to 8	8:15	quarter past 8
	15 minutes to 8		15 minutes after 8
		8:30	half past 8

Tell the time the bus arrives.

Write 8:30 in three other ways.

When the minute hand is on the 6, you can say the time is "half past" the hour.

The bus arrives at *eight thirty*, or *half past eight*, or *30 minutes past eight*.

Tell the time the bus leaves.

Write 2:45 in three other ways.

When the minute hand is on the 9, you can say the time is "15 minutes to" or "quarter to" the hour.

The bus leaves at *two forty-five*, or *15 minutes to three*, or *quarter to three*.

Guided Practice*

MATHEMATICAL PRACTICES

Do you know HOW?

In **1** and **2**, write the time shown on each clock in two ways.

Sample answers are given.

1.

6:45, quarter to 7

2.

15 minutes past 12, quarter past 12

Do you UNDERSTAND?

3. Reason In the example above, why do you think the fraction word "quarter" is used for the time when the minute hand is on the 9?

See margin.

4. The clock shows the time that Etta's skating lesson starts. What time does it start? Give the time in 3 ways.

See margin.

Independent Practice

In **5–7**, write the time shown on each clock in two ways.

Sample answers are given.

5.

9:15, 15 minutes past 9

6.

45 minutes past 10, quarter to 11

7.

3:45, 15 minutes to 4

*For another example, see Set A on page 316.

2 Guided Practice

MATHEMATICAL PRACTICES

Remind students to read a time as quarter past or half past the previous hour, or quarter to the next hour.

Exercise 3

Reason Quantitatively

It can be helpful for some students to visualize a clock face that has been divided into 4 equal parts. Each $\frac{1}{4}$ section equals 15 minutes. It will be easier to see that $\frac{3}{4}$ of an hour is shown with the minute hand on the 9.

Exercise 4

Error Intervention

If students have difficulty giving the time in 3 different ways,

then ask: *How would the same time appear on a digital clock?* [10:15] *How many minutes past the hour is it?* [It is 15 minutes past 10.] *How many quarter hours past the hour is it?* [One; it is quarter past 10.]

Reteaching For another example and more practice, assign **Reteaching** Set A on p. 316.

3 Independent Practice

Remind students that they can give a time as the previous hour, followed by the number of minutes after the hour. When the minute hand is on the 9, students can also say the time is "15 minutes to" or "quarter to" the hour. Use Exercise 7 as an example. *What is the previous hour?* [3:00] *How many minutes past the hour is it?* [45 minutes] *How many minutes to the next hour?* [15 minutes] *Write the time two ways.* [3:45, 15 minutes to 4]

Answers

3. If you start at the top and divide the clock into fourths, one line crosses the number 9.
4. Sample answer: 10:15, quarter past ten, 15 minutes past ten.

3 Develop the Concept

Problem Solving — MATHEMATICAL PRACTICES

Students use underlying processes and mathematical tools for Exercises 11–17. Remind students to check for reasonableness when solving each problem.

Exercise 12
Construct Arguments Some students may have difficulty distinguishing between A.M. and P.M. Tell them that just as "A" precedes "P" in the alphabet, A.M. precedes P.M. in the day. *Which words in the problem indicate that the given time is an A.M. time? Why?* ["Students" and "math test" indicate that the given time is probably during school hours.]

Exercise 16
Model with Mathematics Some students may need help breaking this multiple-step problem down into manageable parts. *Write an expression for the total of Cal and Beth's scores.* [63 + 78] *Write an expression for the total of Rusty and Pang's scores.* [59 + 82] *Write a number sentence that compares the expressions.* [63 + 78 = 59 + 82]

Exercise 17
Test-Taking Tip: Make Smart Choices Encourage students to eliminate wrong answers. *Look at the hour hand on each clock. Which answer choice can you eliminate right away? Explain.* [Answer D shows the hour hand between 2 and 3, which is not close to 7 or 8, so I can eliminate that answer choice.]

Early Finishers Have students look back at Problem 17. Ask them to explain how they decided which choice to circle and which ones not to circle.

Independent Practice

In **8–10**, write the time shown on each clock in two ways.
Sample answers are given.

8. 5:30, half past 5

9. 12:15, quarter past 12

10. 

45 minutes past 3, quarter to 4

Problem Solving — MATHEMATICAL PRACTICES

11. The clocks below show the time that the Flying Horse Carousel in Rhode Island opens and closes. What time does the carousel open? What time does it close?

Opens  Closes 

11:00; 9:00

12. Construct Arguments Mr. Boyd gave his students a math test at 10:45. Explain why this time is most likely an A.M. time.
See margin.

For **13–16**, use the table at the right.

13. Estimation Whose bowling score was about 20 points less than Beth's?
Rusty's

14. Whose bowling score was 15 points more than Cal's?
Beth's

15. What is the order of the friends' names from greatest to least score?
Pang, Beth, Cal, Rusty

Bowling Scores

Name	Score
Cal	63
Beth	78
Rusty	59
Pang	82

16. Model Write a number sentence that compares the total of Cal's and Beth's scores with the total of Rusty's and Pang's scores.
63 + 78 = 59 + 82

17. Ronaldo delivers a newspaper to the Hong family between 7:00 A.M. and 8:00 A.M. each day. Which clock shows a time between 7:00 A.M. and 8:00 A.M.?

(A) 

B 
C 
D 

306

Answer

12. Sample answer: 10:45 P.M. would be in the evening, when school is not open. The test is most likely in the morning during regular school hours.

Enrichment

Roman Numerals

The symbols for numbers, or numerals, used by the ancient Romans are still seen today on some clock faces and buildings. They are used as page numbers at the front of many books, including this one.

Roman numeral	I	V	X	L	C	D	M
Decimal value	1	5	10	50	100	500	1,000

Our number system is called the decimal system. It is based on place value. Roman numerals are based on addition and subtraction.

How to read Roman numerals:

VI = 5 + 1 = 6 When the symbol for the smaller number is written to the right of the greater number, add. No more than three symbols for smaller numbers are used this way.

IV = 5 − 1 = 4 When the symbol for a smaller number is to the left of the greater number, subtract. No more than one symbol for a smaller number is used this way.

Practice

Write each as a decimal number.

1. VII 7
2. XX 20
3. CV 105
4. XIV 14
5. LI 51
6. XXI 21
7. XIX 19
8. DC 600
9. CM 900
10. MC 1,100

Write each as a Roman numeral.

11. 15 XV
12. 30 XXX
13. 9 IX
14. 52 LII
15. 60 LX
16. 6 VI
17. 110 CX
18. 400 CD
19. 550 DL
20. 40 XL

21. **Use Structure** In Roman numerals, the year 1990 is written as MCMXC, and 2007 is written as MMVII. Write the current year using Roman numerals. Check students' answers.

22. One movie was made in the year MMIV. Another movie was made in the year MCML. How many years passed between these years? 54 years

Enrichment

Demonstrate how to use addition to read examples of Roman numerals in which a larger-valued symbol is followed by a smaller-valued symbol. For example:

VI = 5 + 1 = 6
VII = 5 + 1 + 1 = 7
XI = 10 + 1 = 11

Demonstrate how to use subtraction to read examples of Roman numerals in which a smaller-valued symbol is followed by a larger-valued symbol. For example:

IV = 5 − 1 = 4
IX = 10 − 1 = 9
XIV = 10 + (5 − 1) = 14

The complete set of rules for subtracting letters is more involved than what will be addressed at this level. Some of these rules appear below to help guide students.

- Only a single letter that is a power of ten (I, X, and C) is subtracted from a single numeral. So, 45 is XLV (not VL) and 29 is XXIX (not IXXX or XIXX.)
- The greater value cannot be more than ten times the value being subtracted. So IV, IX, XL, and XC are fine, but IC, IL, IM, XD, and XM are not allowed.

However, the official rules for Roman Numerals are not always followed. Some clocks use IIII instead of IV, for example.

Then have students complete the exercises on their own. Discuss Exercise 9. *How do you find what each letter in this Roman numeral stands for?* [Use the table.] *What does the letter C stand for?* [100] *What does the letter M stand for?* [1,000] *Should you use addition or subtraction? Why?* [Subtraction; the C is to the left of a letter that stands for a greater value.] *What numbers do you subtract?* [1,000 − 100] *So, what is the value of CM?* [900]

Extend the activity by having students write a problem using a Roman numeral to stand for their age and a Roman numeral to stand for the age of someone else (the ages should be different). Have them write a problem that can be solved by adding or subtracting the two ages. Students can trade problems with a partner to solve.

4 Close/Assess and Differentiate

Close

Essential Understanding Time can be given to the nearest half hour or quarter before or after the hour. Time can be expressed using different units that are related to each other. A.M. and P.M. are used to designate certain time periods. ***In this lesson you learned how to tell time to the nearest half or quarter hour and how to use reasoning to determine whether to use A.M. or P.M. after a given time.***

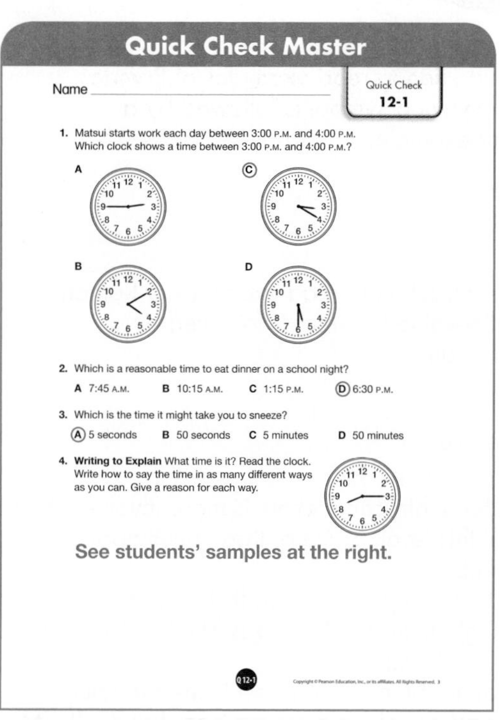

Quick Check Master

Name ______________________ Quick Check 12-1

1. Matsui starts work each day between 3:00 P.M. and 4:00 P.M. Which clock shows a time between 3:00 P.M. and 4:00 P.M.?

A Ⓒ B D

2. Which is a reasonable time to eat dinner on a school night?

A 7:45 A.M. B 10:15 A.M. C 1:15 P.M. Ⓓ 6:30 P.M.

3. Which is the time it might take you to sneeze?

Ⓐ 5 seconds B 50 seconds C 5 minutes D 50 minutes

4. **Writing to Explain** What time is it? Read the clock. Write how to say the time in as many different ways as you can. Give a reason for each way.

See students' samples at the right.

Formative Assessment

Use the **Quick Check** to assess students' understanding.

ASSESSMENT

Exercises 1–3 are worth 1 point each.
Use the rubric to score Exercise 4.

Exercise 4

Writing to Explain Students should read the time on an analog clock face and express it in as many different ways as possible.

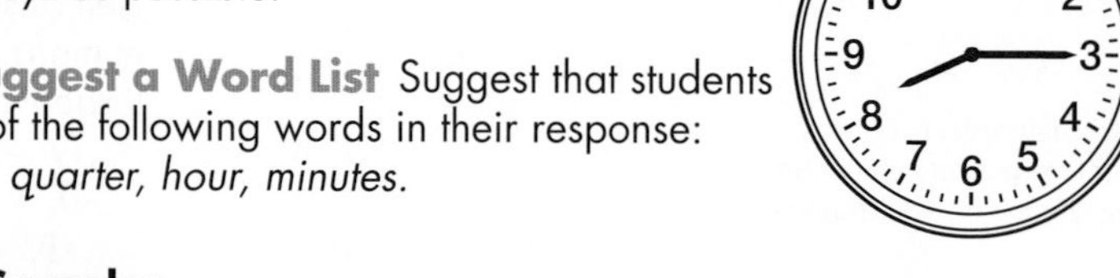

ELL Suggest a Word List Suggest that students use some of the following words in their response: *past, after, quarter, hour, minutes.*

Student Samples

3-point answer The student expresses the given time in four distinct ways correctly, and clearly explains the reasoning.

> The hour hand is between 8 and 9, but it is closer to 8. The minute hand points to 3. Count by 5s for the number of minutes after 8. So it's 15 minutes past 8. 1 hour = 60 minutes, so 15 minutes = $\frac{1}{4}$ hour. So it's also quarter past 8. The digital way to give the time is 8:15 ("eight fifteen"). My dad would say "quarter after 8."

2-point answer The student expresses the given time in three distinct ways correctly, and adequately explains the reasoning.

> Here are different ways to say this time:
> 8:15 (the digital way)
> 15 past 8 (15 minutes after exactly 8 o'clock)
> quarter past 8 (the minute hand has gone $\frac{1}{4}$ of the way around the circle it travels in 1 hour).

1-point answer The student expresses the given time correctly in one way, but has given little or no explanation.

> It is 8:15, or fifteen minutes after 8.

Prescription for Differentiated Instruction

Use student work on the **Quick Check** to prescribe differentiated instruction.

Points	Prescription
0–4	Intervention
5	On-Level
6	Advanced

Differentiated Instruction

Intervention

Quarter Hours

Materials Clock face (Teaching Tool 25) (*per student*)

- Draw a clock face on the board. Draw lines to divide it into 4 quarter hours.
- Ask students to identify the quarter hours and the half hours.
- Draw hands on the clock to show the time as 6:45 and discuss as a group two ways to say the time shown.
- Have Partner 1 show a time on his or her clock face with the minute hand on 3, 6, or 9.
- Then, have Partner 2 tell two ways to say the time on the clock face.
- Last, have students switch roles and repeat the activity.

On-Level

Practice | On-Level | Center Activity

Clip and Cover

Get Started: Get 10 squares in one color and 10 in another color, one paper clip, and one number cube. Take turns.

At Your Turn: Toss one cube to find your oval. **EXAMPLE:** Choose the 3rd oval on the left, **or** choose the 3rd oval on the right. Mark your oval with a paper clip.

How to Play: Tell the time on the clock that you chose. Find the same time on the game board. Cover the answer. Lose your turn if the answer is taken.

How to Win: The first player or team to get any three connected rectangles in a row or column wins.

quarter to ten	eight fifteen	half past eleven	quarter to four
twelve fifteen	five thirty	six thirty	nine forty-five
quarter past ten	half past six	two forty-five	seven thirty
four fifteen	twelve forty-five	quarter past eight	ten fifteen

Left ovals: (clock), 9:45, (clock), 11:30, (clock), 6:30
Right ovals: 10:15, (clock), 3:45, (clock), 8:15, (clock)

If you have more time: Play again! Find another way to say the time on the game board before you cover that time.

Center Activity ★ 12-1

Advanced

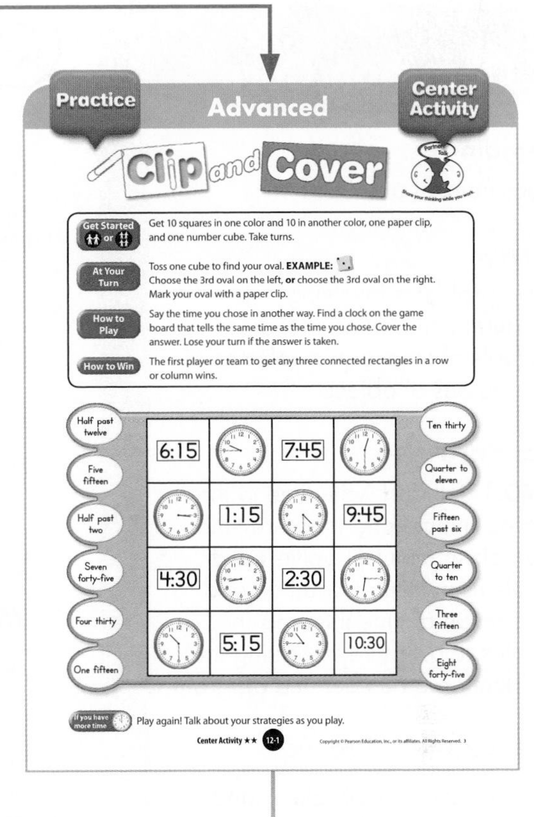
Practice | Advanced | Center Activity

Clip and Cover

Get Started: Get 10 squares in one color and 10 in another color, one paper clip, and one number cube. Take turns.

At Your Turn: Toss one cube to find your oval. **EXAMPLE:** Choose the 3rd oval on the left, **or** choose the 3rd oval on the right. Mark your oval with a paper clip.

How to Play: Say the time you chose in another way. Find a clock on the game board that tells the same time as the time you chose. Cover the answer. Lose your turn if the answer is taken.

How to Win: The first player or team to get any three connected rectangles in a row or column wins.

6:15	(clock)	7:45	(clock)
(clock)	1:15	(clock)	9:45
4:30	(clock)	2:30	(clock)
(clock)	5:15	(clock)	10:30

Left ovals: Half past twelve, Five fifteen, Half past two, Seven forty-five, Four thirty, One fifteen
Right ovals: Ten thirty, Quarter to eleven, Fifteen past six, Quarter to ten, Three fifteen, Eight forty-five

If you have more time: Play again! Talk about your strategies as you play.

Center Activity ★★ 12-1

ELL Report Back To check understanding, ask a student to repeat and complete this sentence: ***Another way to say quarter to eleven is ____.*** [Fifteen minutes before eleven or ten forty-five]

Leveled Homework

Reteaching Master

Name ____________ Reteaching 12-1

Time to the Half Hour and Quarter Hour

An hour is 60 minutes long. A half hour is 30 minutes long. A quarter hour is 15 minutes long.

The A.M. hours are the hours from 12 midnight to 12 noon.
The P.M. hours are the hours from 12 noon to 12 midnight.

The clocks show three different times.

9:30	12:15	1:45
nine thirty	twelve fifteen	one forty-five
half past nine	15 minutes after 12	45 minutes after 1
	quarter after 12	15 minutes to 2
		quarter to 2

Write the time shown on each clock in two ways.

1. 1:15, quarter after 1
2. three forty-five, quarter to 4
3. 2:30, half past 2
4. How many minutes are there in three quarters of an hour? Explain your answer.
45 minutes; Sample Answer: There are 15 minutes in a quarter hour, so add 15 + 15 + 15.

R 12-1

Also available in print

Practice Master

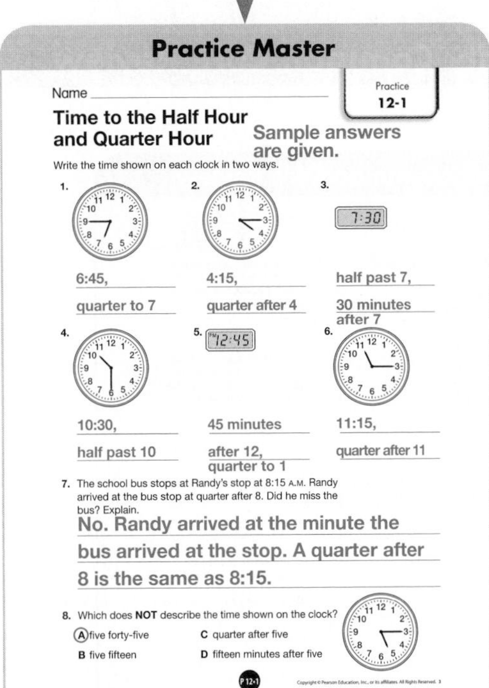
Name ____________ Practice 12-1

Time to the Half Hour and Quarter Hour Sample answers are given.

Write the time shown on each clock in two ways.

1. 6:45, quarter to 7
2. 4:15, quarter after 4
3. 7:30 — half past 7, 30 minutes after 7
4. 10:30, half past 10
5. 12:45 — 45 minutes after 12, quarter to 1
6. 11:15, quarter after 11
7. The school bus stops at Randy's stop at 8:15 A.M. Randy arrived at the bus stop at quarter after 8. Did he miss the bus? Explain.
No. Randy arrived at the minute the bus arrived at the stop. A quarter after 8 is the same as 8:15.
8. Which does **NOT** describe the time shown on the clock?
(A) five forty-five
B five fifteen
C quarter after five
D fifteen minutes after five

P 12-1

Also available in print

Enrichment Master

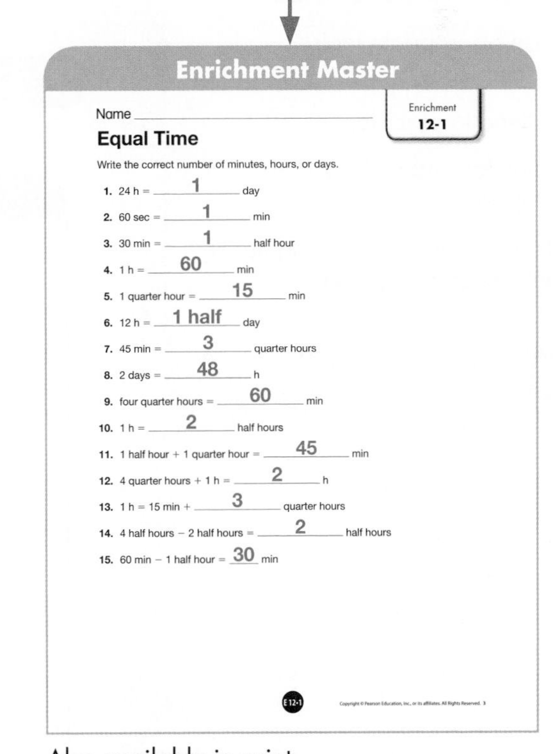
Name ____________ Enrichment 12-1

Equal Time

Write the correct number of minutes, hours, or days.

1. 24 h = 1 day
2. 60 sec = 1 min
3. 30 min = 1 half hour
4. 1 h = 60 min
5. 1 quarter hour = 15 min
6. 12 h = 1 half day
7. 45 min = 3 quarter hours
8. 2 days = 48 h
9. four quarter hours = 60 min
10. 1 h = 2 half hours
11. 1 half hour + 1 quarter hour = 45 min
12. 4 quarter hours + 1 h = 2 h
13. 1 h = 15 min + 3 quarter hours
14. 4 half hours − 2 half hours = 2 half hours
15. 60 min − 1 half hour = 30 min

E 12-1

Also available in print

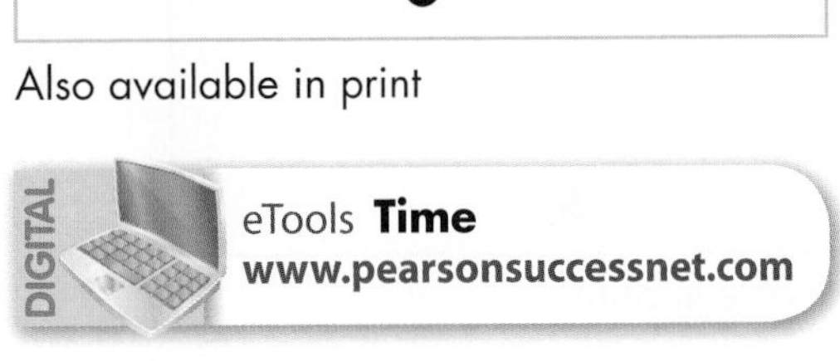

eTools **Time**
www.pearsonsuccessnet.com

Lesson

12-2

Common Core

Domain

Measurement and Data

Cluster

Solve problems involving measurement and estimation of intervals of time, liquid volumes, and masses of objects.

Standard

3.MD.1 Tell and write time to the nearest minute and measure time intervals in minutes. Solve word problems involving addition and subtraction of time intervals in minutes, e.g., by representing the problem on a number line diagram.

Mathematical Practices

- ○ Make sense of problems and persevere in solving them.
- ✔ Reason abstractly and quantitatively.
- ○ Construct viable arguments and critique the reasoning of others.
- ○ Model with mathematics.
- ○ Use appropriate tools strategically.
- ✔ Attend to precision.
- ○ Look for and make use of structure.
- ○ Look for and express regularity in repeated reasoning.

Time to the Minute

Lesson Overview

Objective	Essential Understanding	Vocabulary	Materials
Students will tell time to the nearest minute using analog and digital clocks.	The minute hand takes 5 minutes to move from one number to the next on a typical clock face. The minute hand takes 1 minute to move from one mark to the next on a typical clock face.		Clock face (Teaching Tool 25)

Math Background

Some students may wonder why it is necessary to tell time to the nearest minute. Discuss different situations that require times to be expressed in more precise units. Television schedules usually show times to the nearest half hour. Movie schedules in the paper usually show times to the nearest quarter hour or 5 minutes. Train, bus, and school class schedules can show times to the nearest minute. Clocks at sporting events can show time to the nearest second, or sometimes even tenth or hundredth of a second.

1 Daily Common Core Review

Daily Common Core Review

Name ______________ Daily Common Core Review 12-2

Choose the best answer.

1. Which time is different from the others?
   - A quarter to 4
   - B [clock]
   - C 3:45
   - (D) three fifteen
2. A building is 872 feet tall. Mr. Hernandez rounded the number to the nearest hundred. What number did Mr. Hernandez use?
   - (A) 900
   - B 880
   - C 870
   - D 800
3. Which is the missing number in the pattern below?

   63, 55, 47, ____
   - A 38
   - (B) 39
   - C 40
   - D 41
4. Jenny made 6 baskets for every two her sister made. If her sister made 6 baskets, how many did Jenny make?

   18
5. **Mental Math** A shirt's original price was $40. It is on sale for $12 less than the original price. What is the sale price of the shirt?

   $28
6. What is the name of this polygon?

   Pentagon
7. Sissy baked 48 cookies for 6 of her friends. Each friend will receive the same number of cookies. How many cookies will each friend get?

   8

D 12-2

Also available in print

Content Reviewed

Exercise 1	Time
Exercise 2	Round Whole Numbers
Exercise 3	Number Patterns
Exercise 4	Multiplying Whole Numbers
Exercise 5	Compute Mentally
Exercise 6	Polygons
Exercise 7	Division

2 Develop the Concept: Interactive

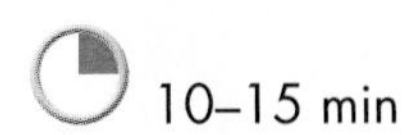

Problem-Based Interactive Learning

Overview Students show and tell time to the minute on a pupil clock face.

Focus How do you tell time to the nearest minute?

Materials Clock face (1 per group), blank clock faces (Teaching Tool 25)

Set the Purpose *You have learned to tell time to the half hour and quarter hour. Today, you will learn to tell time to the minute.*

Connect *What are some examples of exact times of events?* [A movie starts at 8:05, math class starts at 10:35.]

Attend to Precision
Remind students to use the minute hand to tell time to the nearest minute.

Pose the Problem *An airplane is scheduled to arrive at 8:47. How can you use a clock to show this time?* Have students use a pupil clock face and Teaching Tool 25 to show and record the time. Have several students show their clock faces and explain how they found the time.

Whole-Class Discussion *Where does the hour hand point?* [Between 8 and 9] *Where should the minute hand point to show 8:47?* [Two marks beyond the 9] Remind students that it takes the minute hand 5 minutes to move from one number to the next, and it takes the minute hand 1 minute to move from one mark to the next. *What are some different ways to read this time?* Record students' answers on the board. [Eight forty-seven; 47 minutes past 8; 13 minutes to 9]

Small-Group Interaction *Show 8:48 and then 8:51 on your clock. Write each time three different ways. Then take turns showing any time, and have your partner(s) write the time in number form and word form. Switch roles after showing and recording two clock times.*

A bus will arrive at 10:05. Another bus will arrive after every 12 minutes. On a clock face, show each time a bus will arrive, up to 11:00. Record each time in digital (or number) form. [10:17, 10:29, 10:41, 10:53]

3 Develop the Concept: Visual

Visual Learning

Time to the Minute

How do you tell time to the nearest minute?

The clock shows the time a train is scheduled to arrive at Pinewood Station. What time is the train scheduled to arrive? Give the time in digital form and in two other ways.

Look at the picture of the clock face. Where does the minute hand point on the clock? [Between the 8 and the 9] *How is this position of the minute hand different from what you saw in the last lesson?* [The minute hand is pointing between two numbers instead of pointing to a number.] *How do you think you can tell the time?* [Count the minutes.]

Step 1

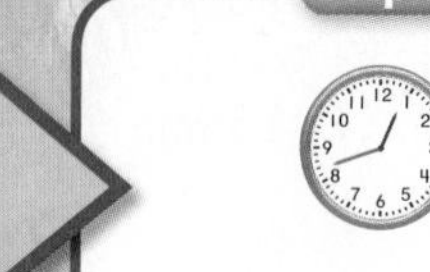

The hour hand is between 12 and 1. The time is after 12:00 and before 1:00.

1 Visual Learning

Set the Purpose Call students' attention to the **Visual Learning Bridge** at the top of the page. *In this lesson you will learn to tell time to the nearest minute.*

2 Guided Practice

MATHEMATICAL PRACTICES

Remind students that the longer hand on a clock is the minute hand and the shorter hand is the hour hand.

Exercise 3
Error Intervention

If students have difficulty explaining,

then ask: *How many minutes are in one hour?* [60 minutes] *How many minutes of the 60 minute hour have passed since 12:00?* [42 minutes] *How many minutes are left until 1:00?* [18 minutes]

Reteaching Draw an analog clock showing 1:23. Explain to students how to give the time in digital form and in two other ways. For another example and more practice, assign **Reteaching** Set B on p. 316.

3 Independent Practice

Remind students that a time can be written as the number of minutes past the hour or as the number of minutes until the next hour. Use Exercise 7 as an example. *How many hours and minutes does the clock show?* [8 hours, 44 minutes, or 8:44] *How many minutes are there until 9:00?* [16 minutes to 9]

Lesson 12-2

Common Core

3.MD.1 Tell and write time to the nearest minute and measure time intervals in minutes. Solve word problems involving addition and subtraction of time intervals in minutes, e.g., by representing the problem on a number line diagram.

Time to the Minute

How do you tell time to the nearest minute?

The clock shows the time a train is scheduled to arrive at Pinewood Station. What time is the train scheduled to arrive? Give the time in digital form and in two other ways.

Guided Practice*

MATHEMATICAL PRACTICES

Do you know HOW?

In **1** and **2**, write the time shown on each clock in two ways. **Sample answers are given.**

1\. 3:12, 12 minutes past 3

2\.

43 minutes past 5, 17 minutes to 6

Do you UNDERSTAND?

3\. **Reason** In the example above, why is 42 minutes past 12 the same as 18 minutes to 1? Explain. **See margin.**

4\. The clock below shows the time that an airplane landed. Write the time in two ways.

10:26; 26 minutes past 10

Independent Practice

In **5–7**, write the time shown on each clock in two ways. **Sample answers are given.**

5\.

11:20, 20 minutes past 11

6\.

39 minutes past 7, 21 minutes to 8

7\.

8:44, 16 minutes to 9

*For another example, see Set B on page 316.

Answer

3. The first time tells how many minutes after the hour. The second time tells how many minutes before the next hour. When the minute hand reaches 12, the time will be 1:00. If you count back from 12 to the minute hand, there are 18 minutes.

Visual Learning Animation

www.pearsonsuccessnet.com or CD

How far does the hour hand move in 1 hour? [From one number to the next number] *How far does the minute hand move in 1 hour?* [All the way around the clock]

Step 2

In 5 minutes, the minute hand moves from one number to the next.

Count by 5s from the 12 to the 8: 40 minutes

Why will skip counting help you find the time? [It will tell me how many minutes past the hour it is.]

Step 3

In 1 minute, the minute hand moves from one mark to the next. After counting by 5s, count two minutes more.

The digital time is 12:42. It is 42 minutes past 12 or 18 minutes to 1.

Prevent Misconceptions
Some students might have trouble counting by 5s and transitioning to counting by ones. Practice skip counting by 5s, stopping at numbers between 15 and 55. Then transition to counting by ones. For example, 5, 10, 15, 20, 21, 22, 23.

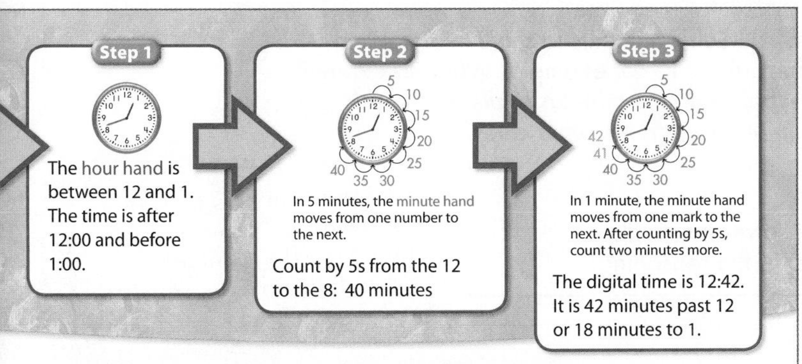

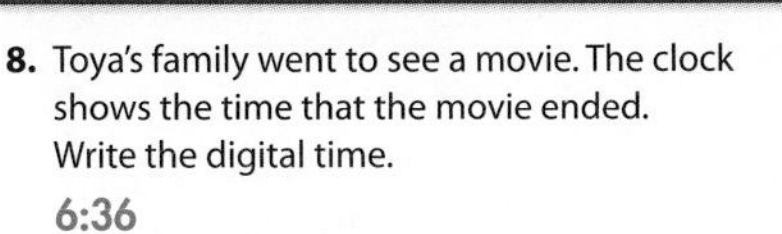

8. Toya's family went to see a movie. The clock shows the time that the movie ended. Write the digital time.
6:36

9. Be Precise The Hubble Space Telescope has been moving in its orbit for 1 hour. In 37 more minutes it will complete an orbit. How many minutes does it take the Hubble Space Telescope to complete 1 orbit?
97 minutes

For **10** and **11**, use the sign at the right.

Winter Sale	
Blanket	$19
Hat	$12
Scarf	$18
Shovel	$23

10. Reason Roy says that a scarf and a hat together cost about the same as a blanket and a hat. Is his estimate reasonable? Explain.
Yes; check students' explanations.

11. What did Jorge buy at the sale if $19 + $19 + $19 + $23 stands for the total cost?
3 blankets and a shovel

12. Ross walks his dog between 3:15 P.M. and 4:00 P.M. Which clock shows a time between 3:15 P.M. and 4:00 P.M.?

A  (B)  C  D 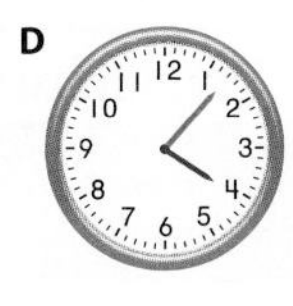

Problem Solving — MATHEMATICAL PRACTICES

Students use underlying processes and mathematical tools for Exercises 8–12. Remind students to check for reasonableness when solving each problem.

Exercise 9
Attend to Precision Students may not recognize the term *orbit.* Draw an oval or ellipse (orbital path) made by a smaller circle (moon) around a larger circle (planet). *An orbit is the path one object makes around another object in space while under the influence of a force such as gravity. For example, the Moon moves in an orbit around Earth. One orbit is one complete trip around. How long does it take the Hubble Space Telescope to complete 1 orbit?* [1 hour, 37 minutes]

Exercise 10
Reason Quantitatively Students should see that the difference between the cost of the blanket and the cost of the scarf is only $1. Since the cost of the hat is part of each comparison, the estimate for the cost of both pairs of items is about the same.

Exercise 12
Test-Taking Tip: Understand the Question Remind students to look for important words. *The word between means you are looking for a time after 3:15 P.M. and before 4:00 P.M.*

Early Finishers Challenge students to draw the clock numbers and the markings for each minute interval on a clock face in the shape of a regular hexagon.

4 Close/Assess and Differentiate

Close

Essential Understanding The minute hand takes 5 minutes to move from one number to the next on a typical clock face. The minute hand takes 1 minute to move from one mark to the next on a typical clock face. *In this lesson you learned how to tell time to the nearest minute.*

ASSESSMENT

Exercises 1–3 are worth 1 point each.
Use the rubric to score Exercise 4.

Exercise 4

Writing to Explain Students should solve a logic riddle about time and express the answer as minutes after the hour and before the next hour.

ELL Model Thinking Aloud Guide students to solve this problem by modeling how they might think about it. For example: *What do I know? What must the hour digit be? What could the minutes digits be? Which of those digits would give a sum of 6 and fit the other clues?*

Student Samples

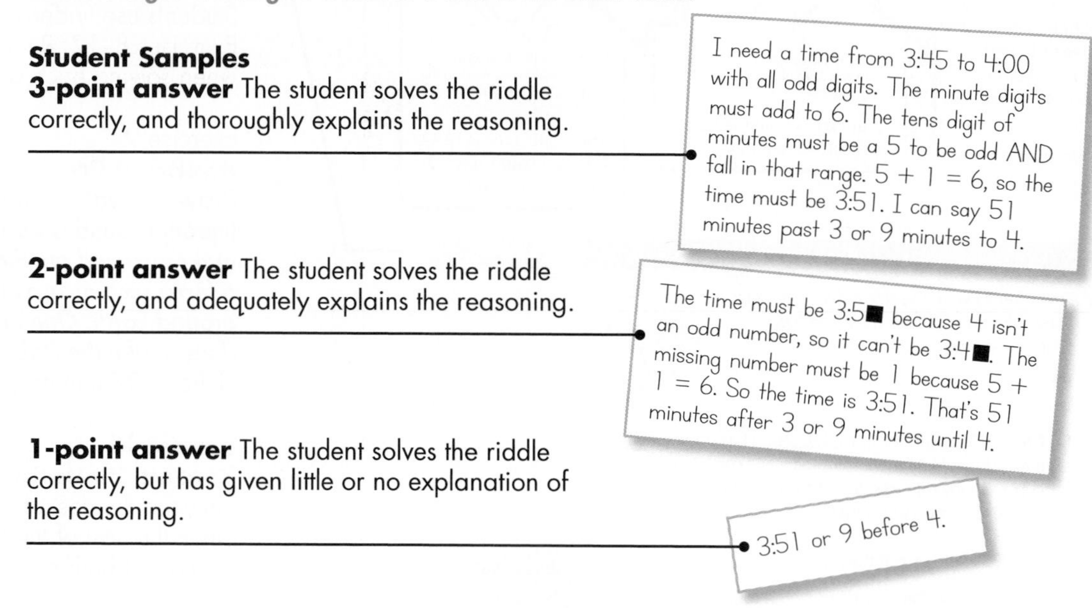

3-point answer The student solves the riddle correctly, and thoroughly explains the reasoning.

2-point answer The student solves the riddle correctly, and adequately explains the reasoning.

1-point answer The student solves the riddle correctly, but has given little or no explanation of the reasoning.

Quick Check Master

Name ________________ Quick Check 12-2

1. Lizzie goes to sleep between 8:15 P.M. and 8:45 P.M. on a school night. Which clock shows a time between 8:15 P.M. and 8:45 P.M.?

A C (B) D

2. The clock below shows the time when Evan called his mom. What time was it?

A 3:06 C 3:13
(B) 3:12 D 3:17

3. After dinner, Margo read for 33 minutes. The clock said 7:49 when she stopped. What time did she start reading?

(A) 7:16
B 7:26
C 7:36
D 8:22

4. **Writing to Explain** Ty got home from school after 3:45 but before 4:00. All the digits in the time were odd numbers. The minutes digits had a sum of 6. What time was it? Explain your thinking. Give the time two ways: *after* the hour and *before* the next hour.

See students' samples at the right.

Formative Assessment

Use the **Quick Check** to assess students' understanding.

Prescription for Differentiated Instruction
Use student work on the **Quick Check** to prescribe differentiated instruction.

Points	Prescription
0–4	Intervention
5	On-Level
6	Advanced

Differentiated Instruction

Intervention

Minutes Count

 10 min 

Materials Clock face (Teaching Tool 25) (*per student*)

- Discuss with students how many minutes are in an hour, a half hour, and a quarter hour.
- Then ask students how many minutes are between every two consecutive numbers on the clock face.
- Show 2:19 on a clock face. Discuss how to read the time on the clock face by skip counting.
- Have Partner 1 show a time on his or her clock.
- Have Partner 2 tell two ways to say the time on the clock.
- Have students switch roles and repeat the activity.

Practice On-Level Center Activity

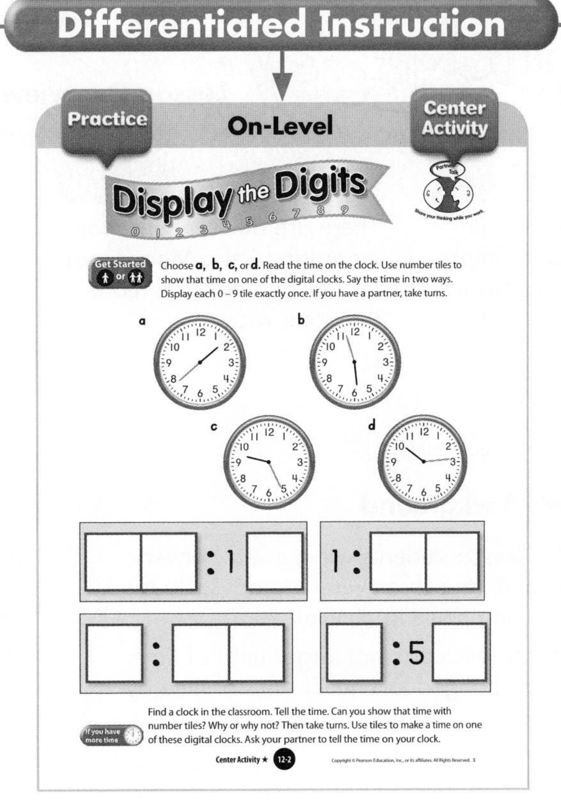

Display the Digits

Get Started: Choose **a**, **b**, **c**, or **d**. Read the time on the clock. Use number tiles to show that time on one of the digital clocks. Say the time in two ways. Display each 0 – 9 tile exactly once. If you have a partner, take turns.

If you have more time: Find a clock in the classroom. Tell the time. Can you show that time with number tiles? Why or why not? Then take turns. Use tiles to make a time on one of these digital clocks. Ask your partner to tell the time on your clock.

Center Activity ★ 12-2

Practice Advanced Center Activity

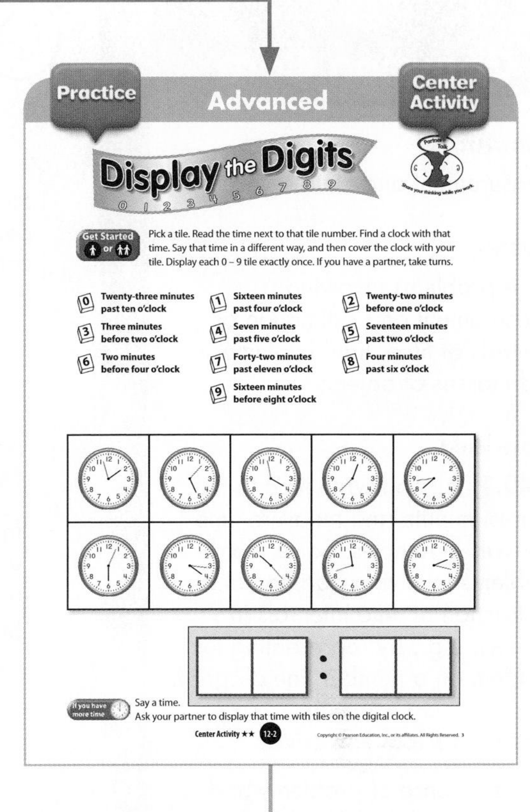

Display the Digits

Get Started: Pick a tile. Read the time next to that tile number. Find a clock with that time. Say that time in a different way, and then cover the clock with your tile. Display each 0 – 9 tile exactly once. If you have a partner, take turns.

0 Twenty-three minutes past ten o'clock
1 Sixteen minutes past four o'clock
2 Twenty-two minutes before one o'clock
3 Three minutes before two o'clock
4 Seven minutes past five o'clock
5 Seventeen minutes past two o'clock
6 Two minutes before four o'clock
7 Forty-two minutes past eleven o'clock
8 Four minutes past six o'clock
9 Sixteen minutes before eight o'clock

If you have more time: Say a time. Ask your partner to display that time with tiles on the digital clock.

Center Activity ★★ 12-2

ELL Report Back To check understanding, ask a student to repeat and complete this sentence: ***When it is sixteen minutes past seven, the hour hand is between 7 and 8 and the minute hand is between ___.*** [3 and 4]

Leveled Homework

Reteaching Master

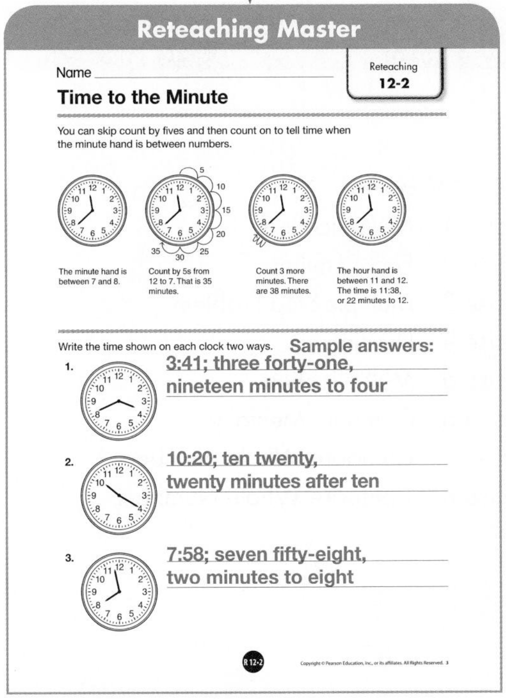

Name ______ Reteaching 12-2

Time to the Minute

You can skip count by fives and then count on to tell time when the minute hand is between numbers.

The minute hand is between 7 and 8. | Count by 5s from 12 to 7. That is 35 minutes. | Count 3 more minutes. There are 38 minutes. | The hour hand is between 11 and 12. The time is 11:38, or 22 minutes to 12.

Write the time shown on each clock two ways. Sample answers:

1. 3:41; three forty-one, nineteen minutes to four
2. 10:20; ten twenty, twenty minutes after ten
3. 7:58; seven fifty-eight, two minutes to eight

R 12-2

Also available in print

Practice Master

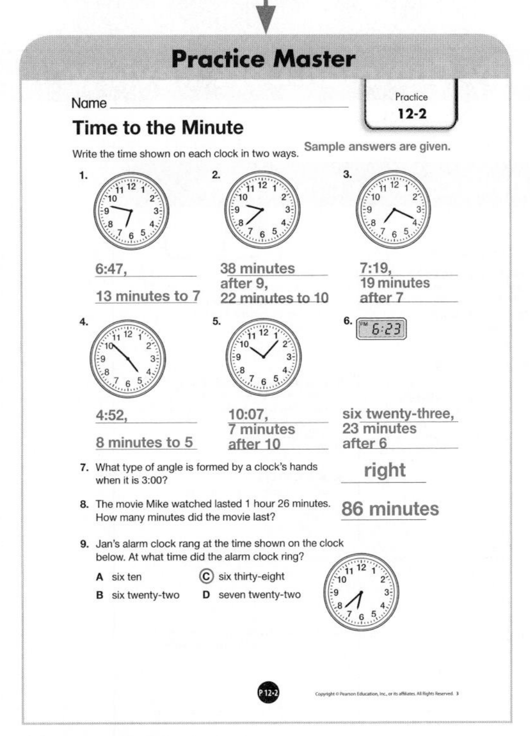

Name ______ Practice 12-2

Time to the Minute

Write the time shown on each clock in two ways. Sample answers are given.

1. 6:47, 13 minutes to 7
2. 38 minutes after 9, 22 minutes to 10
3. 7:19, 19 minutes after 7
4. 4:52, 8 minutes to 5
5. 10:07, 7 minutes after 10
6. 6:23 — six twenty-three, 23 minutes after 6
7. What type of angle is formed by a clock's hands when it is 3:00? right
8. The movie Mike watched lasted 1 hour 26 minutes. How many minutes did the movie last? 86 minutes
9. Jan's alarm clock rang at the time shown on the clock below. At what time did the alarm clock ring?
   A six ten
   B six twenty-two
   (C) six thirty-eight
   D seven twenty-two

P 12-2

Also available in print

Enrichment Master

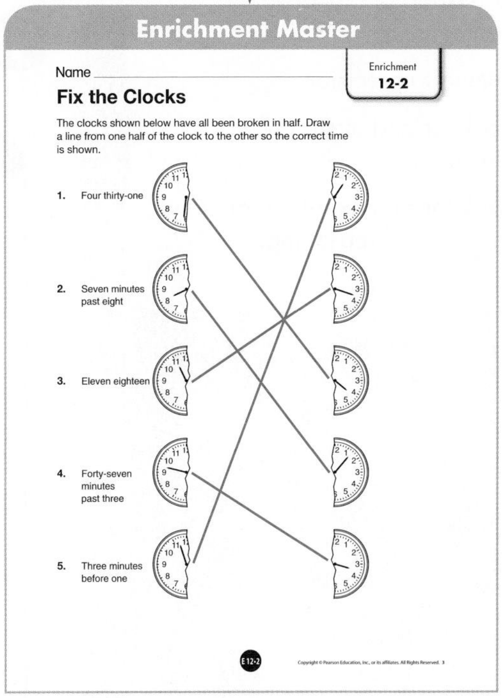

Name ______ Enrichment 12-2

Fix the Clocks

The clocks shown below have all been broken in half. Draw a line from one half of the clock to the other so the correct time is shown.

1. Four thirty-one
2. Seven minutes past eight
3. Eleven eighteen
4. Forty-seven minutes past three
5. Three minutes before one

E 12-2

Also available in print

DIGITAL eTools **Time** **www.pearsonsuccessnet.com**

DIGITAL eTools **Time** **www.pearsonsuccessnet.com**

DIGITAL eTools **Time** **www.pearsonsuccessnet.com**

Lesson

12-3

Common Core

Domain

Measurement and Data

Cluster

Solve problems involving measurement and estimation of intervals of time, liquid volumes, and masses of objects.

Standard

3.MD.1 Tell and write time to the nearest minute and measure time intervals in minutes. Solve word problems involving addition and subtraction of time intervals in minutes, e.g., by representing the problem on a number line diagram.

Mathematical Practices

- ○ Make sense of problems and persevere in solving them.
- ✔ Reason abstractly and quantitatively.
- ✔ Construct viable arguments and critique the reasoning of others.
- ○ Model with mathematics.
- ○ Use appropriate tools strategically.
- ✔ Attend to precision.
- ○ Look for and make use of structure.
- ✔ Look for and express regularity in repeated reasoning.

Units of Time

Lesson Overview

Objective	Essential Understanding	Vocabulary	Materials
Students will perform simple conversions for units of time.	There are different units for measuring time. Many times can be expressed in more than one way.		Calendar (Teaching Tool 26)

Math Background

In this lesson students will convert between units of time such as weeks to days, days to hours, and hours to minutes.

Students will learn that larger units of time can be changed to smaller units of time by multiplying. To correctly convert units, students must know the basic relationships between units of time, such as 1 week = 7 days. To convert 3 weeks to days, multiply 3×7 to get 21 days.

1 Daily Common Core Review

Daily Common Core Review

Name ____________ Daily Common Core Review 12-3

Choose the best answer.

1. Amit brings his mother 7 flowers every day for 1 week. At the end of the week, how many flowers has Amit brought his mother in all?
   (A) 49 C 14
   B 35 D 7

2. Principal Garcia has 64 perfect attendance awards to give. Eight students from each class receive an award, so he divides 64 by 8. Which number sentence is in the same fact family as $64 \div 8 = 8$?
   A $8 \times 3 = 24$ C $8 \times 7 = 56$
   B $8 \times 5 = 40$ (D) $8 \times 8 = 64$

3. In the soccer league, a team receives 3 points for a win, 1 point for a tie, and 0 points for a loss. Mario's team has 6 wins, 1 tie, and 3 losses. How many points does Mario's team have?
   A 7 (C) 19
   B 18 D 22

4. A dodgeball team has 7 players. In Juan's school, 63 students want to form a dodgeball league. How many teams can there be in the league?
   9 teams

5. Jerry works at a gas station and earns $9 per hour. How much money will he earn if he works 4 hours on Friday?
   $36

6. **Mental Math** Larry is filling 3 baskets with 9 eggs. How many eggs will there be in 30 baskets?
   90 eggs

7. Which digit makes the sentence below true?
   415 > 4 [0] 6

8. Sally has 139 books and Anne has 230 books. Who has more books?
   Anne

D 12-3

Also available in print

Content Reviewed

Exercise 1 Multiplication
Exercise 2 Fact Families
Exercise 3 Multiple-Step Problem
Exercise 4 Division
Exercise 5 Multiplication
Exercise 6 Compute Mentally
Exercise 7 Compare Whole Numbers
Exercise 8 Compare Whole Numbers

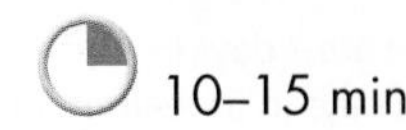
10–15 min

Problem-Based Interactive Learning

Overview Students convert between weeks and days, days and hours, and hours and minutes.

Focus How can you change units of time?

Materials Calendar (Teaching Tool 26), completed for current month (1 per pair)

Set the Purpose *You have learned that time is measured in minutes, hours, days, weeks, and months. Today, you will learn how to change from one unit to another unit when measuring time.*

Connect *One hour from now, you will be [going to lunch]. How many minutes is that?* [60 minutes] *At this time tomorrow, one day will have passed. How many hours is that?* [24 hours] *Next [Tuesday], a week will have passed. How many days is that?* [7 days]

Make Generalizations Students should notice that when using a calendar, each full week has 7 days.

Pose the Problem *A class is going to collect newspapers as part of a recycling project. They will collect newspapers for 3 weeks. How many days are in 3 weeks?* Give students a chance to solve the problem using the month calendar for help.

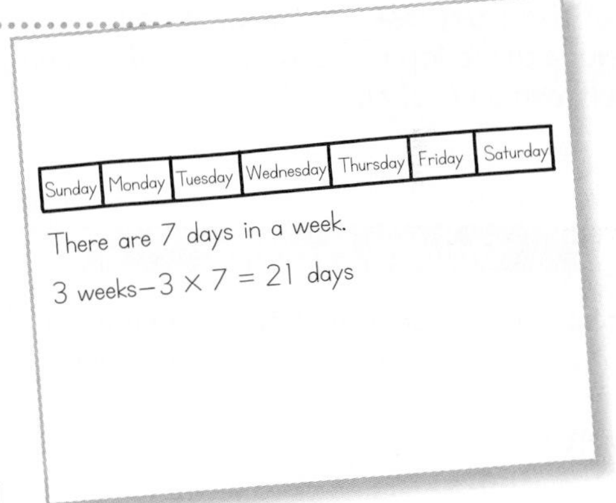

Expand Student Responses Have students share their answers. *How did you find the number of days in 3 weeks?* [I used the calendar to find 3 weeks; then I counted the number of days in 3 weeks.]

Model/Demonstrate On the board, draw a 2-row, 6-column table. Label the first row *Weeks* and the second row *Days*. *How many days are in one week? In 2 weeks? In 3 weeks?* [7, 14, 21] *What pattern do you notice in the table?* [The Number of Days = the Number of Weeks × 7] Develop the idea that this formula can be used for any number of days. Use the formula to find the number of days in 4 and 5 weeks, completing the chart.

Number of Weeks	1	2	3	4	5
Number of Days	7	14	21		

There are 21 days in 3 weeks.

Small-Group Interaction *Work together with a partner to find how many hours are in 4 days, 7 days, and 15 days. Make a table and look for a pattern.* [96 hours in 4 days; 168 hours in 7 days; 360 hours in 15 days]

How many minutes are in half a day? [720 minutes]

3 Develop the Concept: Visual

Visual Learning

Units of Time

How can you change units of time?

The class is growing a plant from a seed. The project will last for 5 weeks. How many days are in 5 weeks? The picture shows how long the seed has been growing. How many hours is this?

Relating Units of Time
1 week (wk) = 7 days
1 day (d) = 24 hours
1 hour (h) = 60 minutes

How many days are in one week? [7 days] *What do you need to find?* [How many days are in 5 weeks] *Look at the units of time in the table. What other units of time can you think of?* [Possible responses: seconds, month, and year]

Since there are 7 days in 1 week, the number of days in 5 weeks is 5×7.

$\square$ days = 5×7 days

$$\begin{array}{r} 7 \\ \times\ 5 \\ \hline 35 \end{array}$$

There are 35 days in 5 weeks.

1 Visual Learning

Set the Purpose Call students' attention to the **Visual Learning Bridge** at the top of the page. *In this lesson you will learn to change between units of time.*

2 Guided Practice

MATHEMATICAL PRACTICES

Point out to students that they are changing from larger units to smaller units, such as changing a given number of weeks to days.

Exercise 3
Error Intervention

If students are unable to change from weeks and days to days,

then show students a calendar and highlight 2 weeks with a marker. *How many days are in 2 weeks?* [14] *What do you need to do to find how many days in 2 weeks and 4 days?* [Change 2 weeks to days, then add the additional 4 days.] Highlight another 4 days on the calendar and have students give the answer. [18 days]

Reteaching Display a calendar and highlight one day. *How many hours are in one day?* [24 hours] Write 24 hours on the highlighted day. Highlight a second day and write 24 hours. *How can you find the number of hours in 6 days?* [Add 24 + 24 + 24 + 24 + 24 + 24] For another example and more practice, assign **Reteaching** Set C on p. 317.

3 Independent Practice

Remind students that they can consult the chart in the Visual Learning Bridge when changing between units of time. Some students may not understand that they need to multiply to convert from a larger unit to a smaller unit. Guide students to see the relationship by helping them make a table for conversions, such as the table for weeks and days shown below.

Number of Weeks	1	2	3	4
Number of Days	7	14	21	28

Lesson 12-3

Common Core

3.MD.1 Tell and write time to the nearest minute and measure time intervals in minutes. Solve word problems involving addition and subtraction of time intervals in minutes, e.g., by representing the problem on a number line diagram.

Units of Time

How can you change units of time?

The class is growing a plant from a seed. The project will last for 5 weeks. How many days are in 5 weeks? The picture shows how long the seed has been growing. How many hours is this?

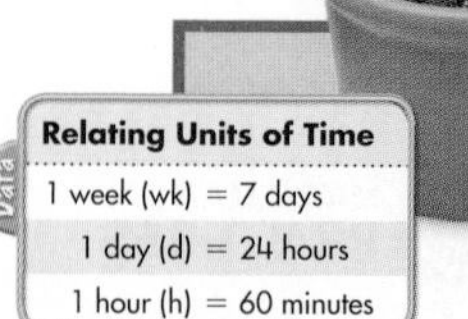

Relating Units of Time
1 week (wk) = 7 days
1 day (d) = 24 hours
1 hour (h) = 60 minutes

Guided Practice*

MATHEMATICAL PRACTICES

Do you know HOW?

For **1–3**, copy and complete to change the units.

1. 8 weeks = $\square$ days
   56 days
2. 2 days = $\square$ hours
   48 hours
3. How many days are in 2 weeks, 4 days?
   18 days

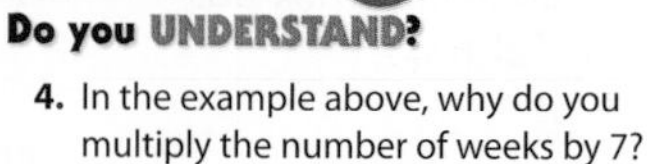

Do you UNDERSTAND?

4. In the example above, why do you multiply the number of weeks by 7?
   There are 7 days in each week.
5. **Reason** At the end of the first week, the class had worked on the science experiment for 6 hours. How many minutes did the class work on the experiment?
   360 minutes

Independent Practice

For **6–15**, copy and complete to change the units.

6. 3 hours = $\square$ minutes
   180 minutes
7. 5 days = $\square$ hours
   120 hours
8. 4 hours = $\square$ minutes
   240 minutes
9. 7 weeks = $\square$ days
   49 days
10. 3 weeks = $\square$ days
    21 days
11. 7 days = $\square$ hours
    168 hours
12. How many hours are in 3 days, 5 hours?
    77 hours
13. How many minutes are in 5 hours, 10 minutes?
    310 minutes
14. How many days are in 10 weeks?
    70 days
15. How many hours are in 9 days?
    216 hours

310 *For another example, see Set C on page 317.

Visual Learning Animation

www.pearsonsuccessnet.com or CD

What operation is used for changing weeks to days? [Multiplication] *If there are 35 days in 5 weeks, how many days are there in 6 weeks?* [6 × 7 = 42 days]

Prevent Misconceptions

Students may not understand the method for changing weeks to days. Have them use a calendar and count the days.

Make a table to find the number of hours in 8 days.

Number of Days	1	2	3	4	5	6	7	8
Number of Hours	24	48	72	96	120	144	168	192

There are 192 hours in 8 days.

What pattern do you see in the table? [As the number of days increases by 1, the number of hours increases by 24.] *How would you use addition to find the number of hours in 10 days?* [10 is three more than 7, so add 24 to 168 three times; 240 hours.]

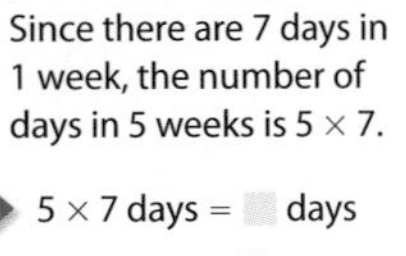

Since there are 7 days in 1 week, the number of days in 5 weeks is 5 × 7.

5 × 7 days = ___ days

$$\begin{array}{r} 7 \\ \times\ 5 \\ \hline 35 \end{array}$$

5 weeks = 35 days

Make a table to find the number of hours in 8 days.

Number of Days	1	2	3	4	5	6	7	8
Number of Hours	24	48	72	96	120	144	168	192

There are 192 hours in 8 days.

Problem Solving — MATHEMATICAL PRACTICES

16. In 30 more minutes, the International Space Station will complete an orbit. It has been in this orbit for 1 hour. How many minutes does it take the International Space Station to complete 1 orbit?
90 minutes

17. A group of high school students helped to prepare samples of materials to send to the International Space Station in 2001. The samples were returned to Earth from space after 4 years. In what year were the samples returned?
2005

For **18** and **19**, use the table at the right.

Spacewalk	
Planned Time	6 hours, 20 minutes
Actual Time	5 hours, 54 minutes

18. Be Precise Astronauts at the International Space Station took a spacewalk to do tasks outside the station. They finished their tasks in less time than was planned. How many minutes of actual time did the astronauts need?
354 minutes

19. Writing to Explain How many fewer minutes than planned did the astronauts need? Explain how you found your answer.
See margin.

20. Communicate A sailfish can swim as fast as 68 miles per hour. In 1 minute can a sailfish swim as far as 1 mile? Explain your answer.
See margin.

21. What fraction of an hour is 20 minutes? Write your answer in simplest form. $\frac{1}{3}$

22. How many days are in 6 weeks?

(A) 42 **B** 36 **C** 13 **D** 7

Problem Solving — MATHEMATICAL PRACTICES

Students use underlying processes and mathematical tools for Exercises 16–22. Remind students to check for reasonableness when solving each problem.

Exercise 18
Attend to Precision Students may forget to add the minutes after converting 5 hours to minutes. Remind students they need to add the additional minutes to the total to find the actual time.

Exercise 22
Test-Taking Tip: Understand the Question Remind students to look for important words. *Which units of measure are you converting?* [Weeks to days]

Early Finishers Write the following on the chalkboard: ____ weeks ____ days. One student fills in the blank with a number. The other student figures out how many total days. Repeat for ____ hours ____ minutes.

Answers

19. 26 minutes; Sample answer: I know 1 h = 60 min so I converted 6 hours, 20 minutes into 5 hours, 80 minutes and subtracted; 5 − 5 = 0 and 80 − 54 = 26.

20. Yes; A speed of 68 mph means the sailfish can swim 68 miles in 60 minutes or more than 1 mile in 1 minute.

4 Close/Assess and Differentiate

Close

Essential Understanding There are different units for measuring time. Many times can be expressed in more than one way. ***In this lesson you learned that you can convert between units of time.***

ASSESSMENT

Exercises 1–3 are worth 1 point each.
Use the rubric to score Exercise 4.

Exercise 4

Writing to Explain Students should choose the operation, use number sense, and apply equivalent time relationships to determine the age of a baby in days.

ELL Suggest a Word List Suggest that students use the following words in their response: *week, day, multiply, half, hours.*

Student Samples

3-point answer The student converts the number of days correctly, and provides a thorough explanation.

2-point answer The student converts the number of days correctly, and provides an adequate explanation.

1-point answer The student answers incorrectly, and explains with few details.

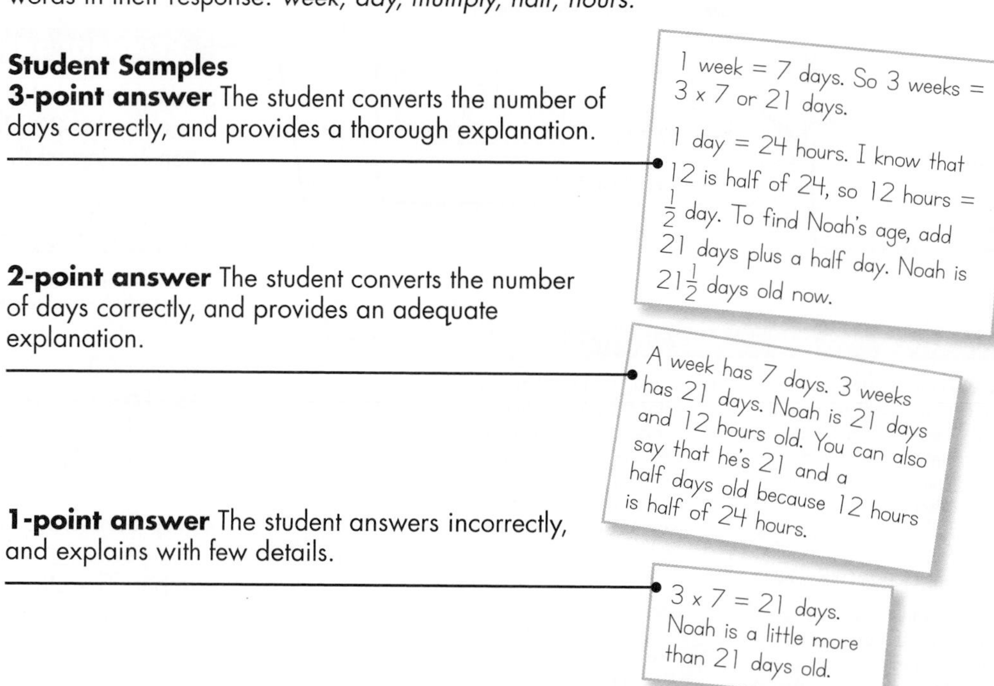

Quick Check Master

Name ____________ Quick Check 12-3

1. How many hours are in 3 days?
   Ⓐ 72 hours
   B 36 hours
   C 24 hours
   D 21 hours

2. Brian's summer vacation lasts for 9 weeks. For how many days will he be on vacation?
   A 16 days
   Ⓑ 63 days
   C 72 days
   D 90 days

3. Gia's favorite movie runs for 108 minutes. How long is the movie in hours and minutes?
   A 1 hour 8 minutes
   B 1 hour 18 minutes
   Ⓒ 1 hour 48 minutes
   D 3 hours 8 minutes

4. **Writing to Explain** Baby Noah was born 3 weeks and 12 hours ago. How old is Noah in days? Explain your thinking and show your work.
   See students' samples at the right.

Q 12-3

Formative Assessment

Use the **Quick Check** to assess students' understanding.

Prescription for Differentiated Instruction
Use student work on the **Quick Check** to prescribe differentiated instruction.

Points	Prescription
0–4	Intervention
5	On-Level
6	Advanced

Differentiated Instruction

Intervention

Converting Units of Time

 10 min 

Materials Calendar (Teaching Tool 26), colored pencils, marker

- Have students use the calendar to color in 3 weeks, 4 days. Ask students to convert the colored-in section to days.
- *How many days did you highlight to represent one week?* [7 days] Have students use a marker to outline each week shown on the calendar. *How many total weeks are there?* [3] *How many days are in 3 weeks?* [21]
- Now have students use the marker to count on for each additional day. *What number do you have in the first additional day?* [22] *How many days in all are 3 weeks, 4 days?* [25]

On-Level

Practice | Center Activity

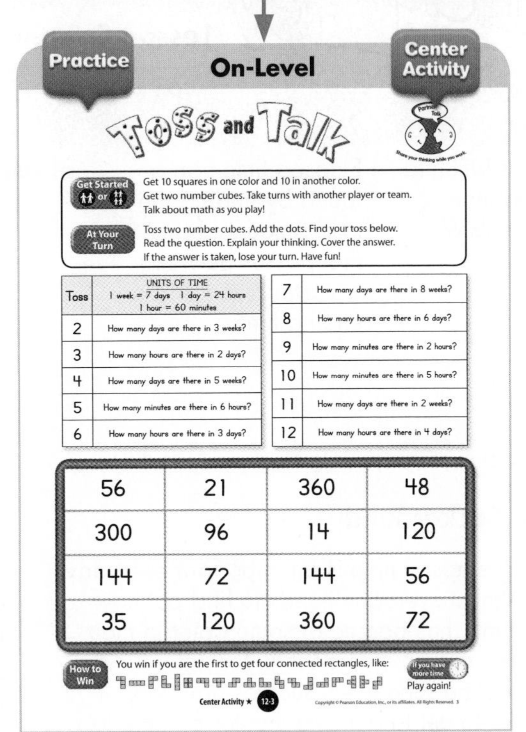

Toss and Talk

Get Started: Get 10 squares in one color and 10 in another color. Get two number cubes. Take turns with another player or team. Talk about math as you play!

At Your Turn: Toss two number cubes. Add the dots. Find your toss below. Read the question. Explain your thinking. Cover the answer. If the answer is taken, lose your turn. Have fun!

Toss	UNITS OF TIME 1 week = 7 days 1 day = 24 hours 1 hour = 60 minutes
2	How many days are there in 3 weeks?
3	How many hours are there in 2 days?
4	How many days are there in 5 weeks?
5	How many minutes are there in 6 hours?
6	How many hours are there in 3 days?
7	How many days are there in 8 weeks?
8	How many hours are there in 6 days?
9	How many minutes are there in 2 hours?
10	How many minutes are there in 5 hours?
11	How many days are there in 2 weeks?
12	How many hours are there in 4 days?

56	21	360	48
300	96	14	120
144	72	144	56
35	120	360	72

How to Win: You win if you are the first to get four connected rectangles, like:

If you have more time: Play again!

Center Activity ★ 12-3

Advanced

Practice | Center Activity

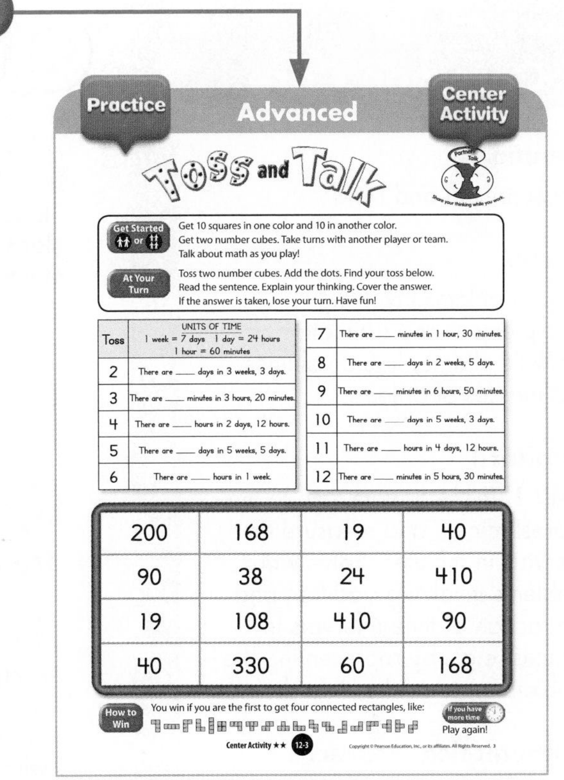

Toss and Talk

Get Started: Get 10 squares in one color and 10 in another color. Get two number cubes. Take turns with another player or team. Talk about math as you play!

At Your Turn: Toss two number cubes. Add the dots. Find your toss below. Read the sentence. Explain your thinking. Cover the answer. If the answer is taken, lose your turn. Have fun!

Toss	UNITS OF TIME 1 week = 7 days 1 day = 24 hours 1 hour = 60 minutes
2	There are ____ days in 3 weeks, 3 days.
3	There are ____ minutes in 3 hours, 20 minutes.
4	There are ____ hours in 2 days, 12 hours.
5	There are ____ days in 5 weeks, 5 days.
6	There are ____ hours in 1 week.
7	There are ____ minutes in 1 hour, 30 minutes.
8	There are ____ days in 2 weeks, 5 days.
9	There are ____ minutes in 6 hours, 50 minutes.
10	There are ____ days in 5 weeks, 3 days.
11	There are ____ hours in 4 days, 12 hours.
12	There are ____ minutes in 5 hours, 30 minutes.

200	168	19	40
90	38	24	410
19	108	410	90
40	330	60	168

How to Win: You win if you are the first to get four connected rectangles, like:

If you have more time: Play again!

Center Activity ★★ 12-3

ELL Report Back To check understanding, ask a student to repeat and complete this sentence: *The number of hours in two days is ____.* [48]

Leveled Homework

Reteaching Master

Name ________ Reteaching 12-3

Units of Time

There are 60 minutes (min) in an hour (h).
There are 24 hours in a day (d).
There are 7 days in a week (wk).

To change from a larger unit to a smaller unit, multiply.

To find the number of hours in 2 days, multiply: 2 × 24 = 48.
So, there are 48 hours in 2 days.

Complete to change the units.

1. 6 weeks = ■ ■ days **42**
2. 3 days = ■ ■ hours **72**
3. How many days are there in 7 weeks? **49**
4. How many minutes are there in 9 hours? **540**
5. How many days are there in 3 weeks, 4 days? **25**
6. How many minutes are there in 4 hours, 30 minutes? **270**
7. **Writing to Explain** Nikki's school day lasts 7 hours, 20 minutes. How many minutes does Nikki's school day last? Explain how you found your answer.
440 minutes; Sample answer: To find the number of minutes in 7 hours, I used a table. For each new hour, there are 60 more minutes (7 h = 420 min). Then I added the extra minutes: 420 + 20 = 440.

R 12-3

Also available in print

Practice Master

Name ________ Practice 12-3

Units of Time

Change the units. Complete.

1. 5 hours = ■ ■ ■ minutes **300**
2. 3 weeks = ■ ■ days **21**
3. 8 weeks = ■ ■ days **56**
4. 6 hours = ■ ■ ■ minutes **360**
5. How many minutes are in 3 hours, 30 minutes? **210**
6. How many days are there in 4 weeks, 3 days? **31**
7. Kendra watched two movies. The first lasted 100 minutes. The second lasted 1 hour, 55 minutes. Which movie was longer? By how many minutes? **The second movie was 15 minutes longer than the first.**
8. **Writing to Explain** How many hours are there in a week? Explain how you found your answer. **168; Sample answer: I added the number of hours in 1 day 7 times because there are 7 days in 1 week.**
9. The Wilson family is going on a 5-week vacation through Australia and New Zealand this summer. How many days will the Wilson's be on vacation? **35 days**
10. Lacy slept 8 hours last night. How many minutes did Lacy sleep?
A 400 C 640
(B) 480 D 800

P 12-3

Also available in print

Enrichment Master

Name ________ Enrichment 12-3

Hours, Days, or Weeks?

You are making a model of a volcano for a science project.

1. You have 8 days to finish the project. Complete the pattern on the calendar. How many hours is that? **192** hours

MARCH

S	M	T	W	T	F	S
1 **24**	2 **48**	3 **72**	4 **96**	5 **120**	6 **144**	7 **168**
8 **192**	9	10	11	12	13	14
15	16	17	18	19	20	21
22	23	24	25	26	27	28
29	30	31				

2. It takes 4 hours for the paint to dry. How many minutes are in 4 hours? **240** minutes
3. Suppose you let the paint dry for 5 hours, 15 minutes. How many minutes are in 5 hours, 15 minutes? **315** minutes
4. Suppose you have been working on the project for 2 days, 9 hours. How many hours did you work on the project? **57** hours
5. You will enter your project in the science fair that takes place in 6 weeks. How many days away is the science fair? **42** days
6. The date for Monday of each week in April is listed. What is the date of the Monday of the fourth week?

Week	1	2	3	4
Date of Monday	April 6	April 13	April 20	?

April 27

E 12-3

Also available in print

DIGITAL eTools **Time** www.pearsonsuccessnet.com

DIGITAL eTools **Time** www.pearsonsuccessnet.com

DIGITAL eTools **Spreadsheet/Data/Grapher** www.pearsonsuccessnet.com

Lesson

12-4

Common Core

Domain

Measurement and Data

Cluster

Solve problems involving measurement and estimation of intervals of time, liquid volumes, and masses of objects.

Standard

3.MD.1 Tell and write time to the nearest minute and measure time intervals in minutes. Solve word problems involving addition and subtraction of time intervals in minutes, e.g., by representing the problem on a number line diagram.

Mathematical Practices

- ○ Make sense of problems and persevere in solving them.
- ✔ Reason abstractly and quantitatively.
- ○ Construct viable arguments and critique the reasoning of others.
- ✔ Model with mathematics.
- ✔ Use appropriate tools strategically.
- ○ Attend to precision.
- ○ Look for and make use of structure.
- ○ Look for and express regularity in repeated reasoning.

Elapsed Time

Lesson Overview

Objective	Essential Understanding	Vocabulary	Materials
Students will find elapsed time in intervals of minutes.	Elapsed time can be found by finding the total amount of time that passes between a starting time and an ending time.	**elapsed time**	Clock face (Teaching Tool 25)

Math Background

Finding elapsed time is an important everyday skill. Almost everyone needs to find out how much time has passed at some point in their lives. For example, it is useful for determining and meeting schedules, such as how long it will take to get to a movie theater on time to meet your friends. It is also a useful skill to be able to determine how much time has passed during a specific activity.

In this lesson, students are introduced to the study of elapsed time with 1-hour and 5-minute intervals. Most students will have had experience in Grade 2 of finding elapsed time in hourly intervals.

Long ago, finding elapsed time using hourly intervals was almost a necessity. For example, one of the first portable timepieces was the sundial, used around 3500 B.C. Called the gnomon, it consisted of a vertical stick that cast a shadow indicating the time of day.

1 Daily Common Core Review

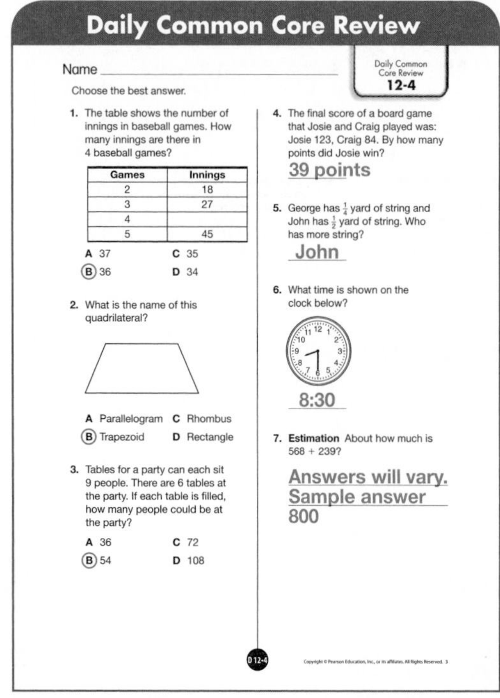

Daily Common Core Review

Name ______________

Daily Common Core Review 12-4

Choose the best answer.

1. The table shows the number of innings in baseball games. How many innings are there in 4 baseball games?

Games	Innings
2	18
3	27
4	
5	45

A 37　(B) 36　C 35　D 34

2. What is the name of this quadrilateral?

A Parallelogram　(B) Trapezoid　C Rhombus　D Rectangle

3. Tables for a party can each sit 9 people. There are 6 tables at the party. If each table is filled, how many people could be at the party?

A 36　(B) 54　C 72　D 108

4. The final score of a board game that Josie and Craig played was: Josie 123, Craig 84. By how many points did Josie win?

39 points

5. George has $\frac{1}{4}$ yard of string and John has $\frac{1}{2}$ yard of string. Who has more string?

John

6. What time is shown on the clock below?

8:30

7. **Estimation** About how much is 568 + 239?

Answers will vary. Sample answer 800

D 12-4

Also available in print

Content Reviewed

Exercise 1	Multiplication Facts
Exercise 2	Quadrilaterals
Exercise 3	Problem Solving
Exercise 4	Subtraction
Exercise 5	Compare Fractions
Exercise 6	Time
Exercise 7	Estimate Sums

2 Develop the Concept: Interactive

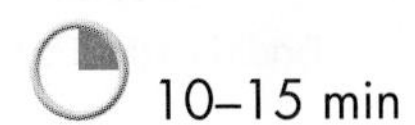

Problem-Based Interactive Learning

Overview Students find elapsed time to the hour and minute.

Focus How can you find elapsed time?

Materials Pupil's clock face or Blank clock faces (Teaching Tool 25) (1 per group or pair)

Vocabulary elapsed time

Set the Purpose *You know how to tell time in hours and minutes. Today, you will learn how to find how much time has passed between a start time and an end time.*

Connect *How can you find out how long your lunch time lasts if you know what time it starts and what time it ends?* [Possible response: You can watch a clock to time how long it lasts; you can count the number of minutes.]

MATHEMATICAL PRACTICES

Use Appropriate Tools Give students a start time and an end time and have them use a clock face to find the elapsed time.

Pose the Problem *Denise went to see a movie. The movie started at 1:00 P.M. It ended at 2:35 P.M. How long did the movie last?* Display both times on clock faces in front of the class. Give students a chance to solve the problem using a clock face to help.

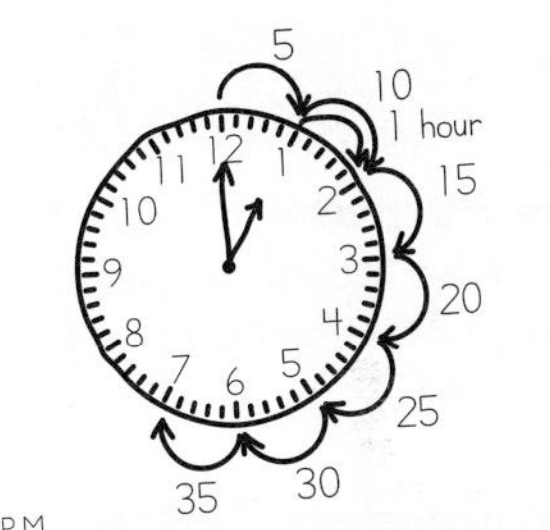

Start at 1:00 P.M.
The hour hand moves from 1 to 2; Count 1 hour.
The minute hand moves to the 7.
Count by 5s: 5, 10, 15, 20, 25, 30, 35 minutes.
The movie lasts 1 hour 35 minutes.

Expand Student Responses Have students share their solutions. *How did you find how long the movie lasted?* [I used the clock to count the hours and minutes that went by; I counted hours first and then added the minutes.]

Model/Demonstrate Use a clock face to model finding how long the movie lasted. Show the start time, 1:00. *I will move the hour hand (the shorter hand) to show the hour passing. At what hour should I stop?* [2 o'clock] *How many hours have passed?* [One] *Now I will move the minute hand (the longer hand) to show the minutes passing. How can you find how many minutes have passed?* [Count by 5s.] *At what minute should I stop?* [35 minutes; at the 7] *Count: 5, 10, 15, 20, 25, 30, 35. So how long did the movie last?* [1 hour, 35 minutes]

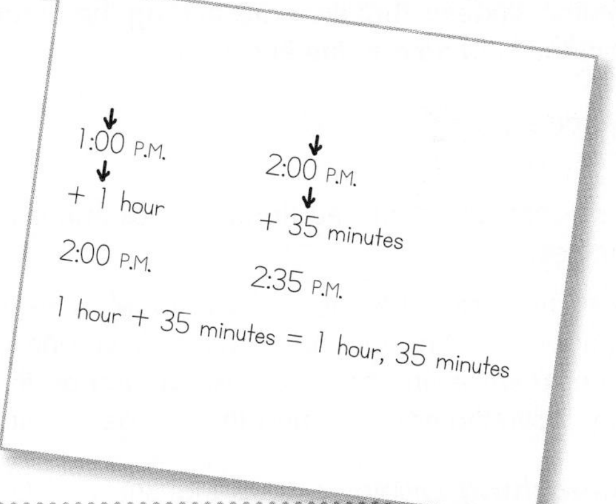

Academic Vocabulary *Elapsed time is the total amount of time that passes from the beginning time to the ending time.*

What if the same movie started at 12:50 P.M.? What time would the movie end? [2:25 P.M.]

3 Develop the Concept: Visual

Visual Learning

Elapsed Time

How can you find elapsed time?

Janey took part in a charity walk. The walk started at 7:00 A.M. It ended at 11:20 A.M. How long did the walk last?

Elapsed time is the total amount of time that passes from the starting time to the ending time.

Look at the clocks. What does the time on the left stand for? [The time the walk started] *What does the time on the right stand for?* [The time the walk ended] *What is another way to describe elapsed time?* [Possible response: How long something lasts]

1 Visual Learning

Set the Purpose Call students' attention to the **Visual Learning Bridge** at the top of the page. *In this lesson you will learn to find the amount of time that passes between a start time and end time, called elapsed time.*

Animated Glossary Students can see highlighted words defined in the Online Student Edition.
elapsed time
www.pearsonsuccessnet.com

2 Guided Practice

MATHEMATICAL PRACTICES

Remind students that they are finding the amount of time that passes from the start time to the end time.

Exercise 2
Error Intervention

If students are confused finding times that involve both hours and minutes,

then have students use a clock model to help them find the answer. Point out that the hour hand moves from one number on the clock to the next while one hour passes. Encourage them to count by 5s as they move the hands to find the number of minutes.

Reteaching Display a clock that shows 1:00. *How much time passes from 1:00 to 5:00?* Demonstrate by moving the hands on the clock. [4 hours] *How much time passes from 5:00 to 5:30?* Demonstrate by moving the minute hand to show 5:30. [30 minutes] *How much total time has passed?* [4 hours and 30 minutes] For another example and more practice, assign **Reteaching** Set D on p. 317.

3 Independent Practice

Watch for students who miscount when finding elapsed time because they begin counting on the hour rather than from the actual starting time. Remind students that both the minute hand and the hour hand must be positioned correctly.

Lesson 12-4

Common Core

3.MD.1 Tell and write time to the nearest minute and measure time intervals in minutes. Solve word problems involving addition and subtraction of time intervals in minutes, e.g., by representing the problem on a number line diagram.

Elapsed Time

How can you find elapsed time?

Janey took part in a charity walk. The walk started at 7:00 A.M. It ended at 11:20 A.M. How long did the walk last?

Start End

Elapsed time is the total amount of time that passes from the starting time to the ending time.

Guided Practice*

MATHEMATICAL PRACTICES

Do you know HOW?

For **1–3**, find the elapsed time.

1. Start Time: 11:00 A.M.
   End Time: 5:00 P.M.
   6 hours
2. Start Time: 1:00 P.M.
   End Time: 4:45 P.M.
   3 hours, 45 minutes
3. Start Time: 7:10 A.M.
   End Time: 8:00 A.M.
   50 minutes

Do you UNDERSTAND?

4. **Reason** In the example above, why do you count the minutes by 5s as the minute hand moves to each number on the clock?
   See margin.
5. During the charity walk, lunch was served from 12:00 P.M. until 2:10 P.M. How long was lunch served?
   2 hours, 10 minutes
6. A movie started at 2:30 P.M. and ran for 1 hour, 45 minutes. What time did the movie end?
   4:15 P.M.

Independent Practice

For **7–15**, find the elapsed time.

7. Start Time: 6:30 P.M.
   End Time: 9:50 P.M.
   3 hours, 20 minutes
8. Start Time: 11:00 A.M.
   End Time: 3:55 P.M.
   4 hours, 55 minutes
9. Start Time: 5:40 P.M.
   End Time: 6:00 P.M.
   20 minutes
10. Start Time: 8:10 A.M.
    End Time: 10:45 A.M.
    2 hours, 35 minutes
11. Start Time: 9:15 A.M.
    End Time: 10:45 A.M.
    1 hour, 30 minutes
12. Start Time: 10:00 A.M.
    End Time: 3:00 P.M.
    5 hours
13. Start Time: 3:20 P.M.
    End Time: 6:00 P.M.
    2 hours, 40 minutes
14. Start Time: 7:30 A.M.
    End Time: 9:45 A.M.
    2 hours, 15 minutes
15. Start Time: 12:45 P.M.
    End Time: 2:20 P.M.
    1 hour, 35 minutes

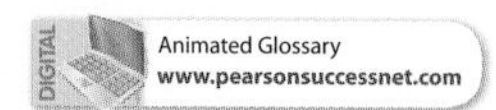

312 *For another example, see Set D on page 317.

Answer

4. It takes the minute hand 5 minutes to move from one number to the next number on the clock.

Visual Learning Animation

www.pearsonsuccessnet.com or CD

How do you know this clock is showing the correct starting time, 7:00? [The hour hand (shorter hand) is on 7 and the minute hand (the longer hand) is on the 12]

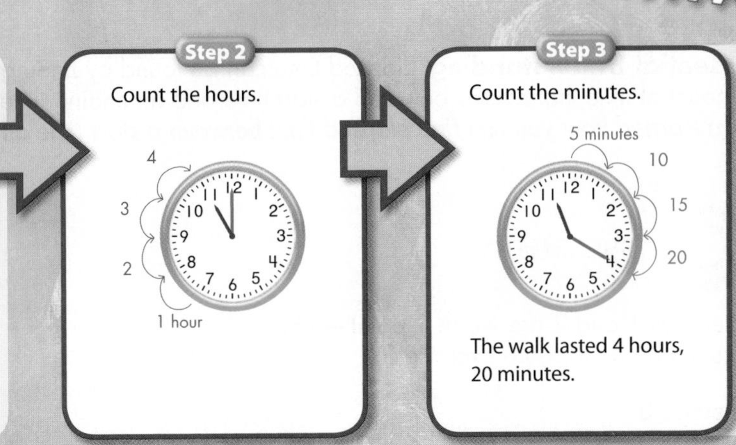

When you count 5, 10, 15, 20, what are you counting? [The minutes that have passed when the minute hand moved from 11 o'clock to 11:20] *How do you get the total amount of time the walk lasted?* [Combine the hours you counted and the minutes you counted.]

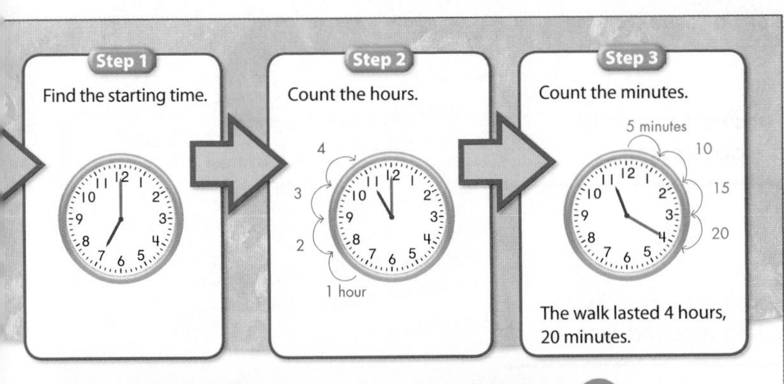

Problem Solving — MATHEMATICAL PRACTICES

16. The picnic started at 12:10 P.M. and ended at 5:00 P.M. How long did the picnic last?
4 hours, 50 minutes

17. The baseball game started at 1:15 P.M. It lasted 2 hours, 45 minutes. What time did the game end?
4:00 P.M.

For **18**, use the number line at right.

18. Model The picnic started at 12:10 P.M. Kevin had arrived 30 minutes later. What time did Kevin arrive?
12:40 P.M.

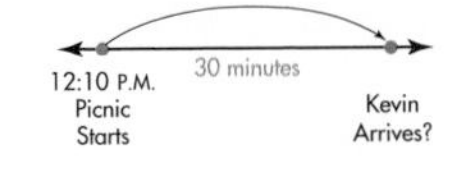

Mrs. Flores keeps a list of the amount of time it takes for different items to bake. Use the table at the right for **19** and **20**.

19. Which items take less than $\frac{1}{2}$ hour to bake?
Bread, granola bars, vegetables

Item	Baking Time in Minutes
Bread	26
Granola Bars	21
Pasta Dish	48
Vegetables	24

20. Estimation About how many more minutes does it take to bake the pasta dish than to bake the granola bars?
About 30 minutes more

21. Model The train leaves Carlton at 9:25 A.M. and stops at Elgin at 10:55 A.M. How long is the ride?

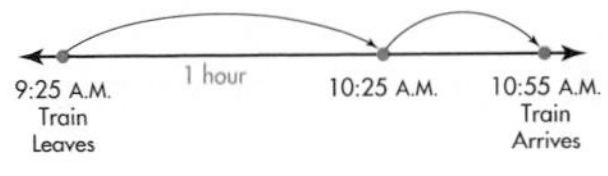

A 1 hour, 20 minutes
B 1 hour, 25 minutes
(C) 1 hour, 30 minutes
D 1 hour, 35 minutes

Lesson 12-4 

Problem Solving — MATHEMATICAL PRACTICES

Students use underlying processes and mathematical tools for Exercises 16–21. Remind students to check for reasonableness when solving each problem.

Exercise 19
Students should recognize that the titles of columns of the data chart give important information. *What information does the data chart provide?* [Different items' baking times in minutes] *Why is this information important?* [You are finding which items take less than $\frac{1}{2}$ hour or 30 minutes to bake.]

Exercise 21
Model with Mathematics Remind students to look for important information. *Between which two times are you finding the elapsed time?* [9:25 A.M. and 10:55 A.M.]

Early Finishers Ask students to write the time that school starts and the time that school ends. Have them find the elapsed time.

4 Close/Assess and Differentiate

Close

Essential Understanding Elapsed time can be found by finding the total amount of time that passes between a start time and an ending time. ***In this lesson you learned how you can find elapsed time between a start time and an end time.***

Exercises 1 and 2 are worth 1 point each.
Use the rubric to score Exercise 3.

Exercise 3

Writing to Explain Students should solve a problem involving elapsed time between a start and end time.

Suggest a Sequence Suggest that students use the following words in their response: *first, then,* and *next.*

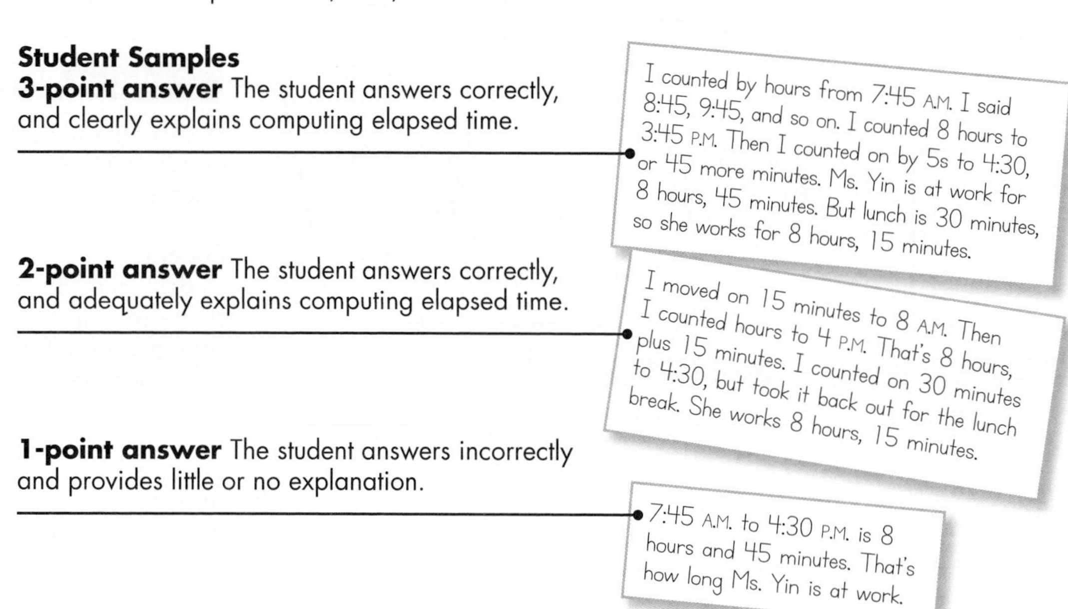

Student Samples

3-point answer The student answers correctly, and clearly explains computing elapsed time.

2-point answer The student answers correctly, and adequately explains computing elapsed time.

1-point answer The student answers incorrectly and provides little or no explanation.

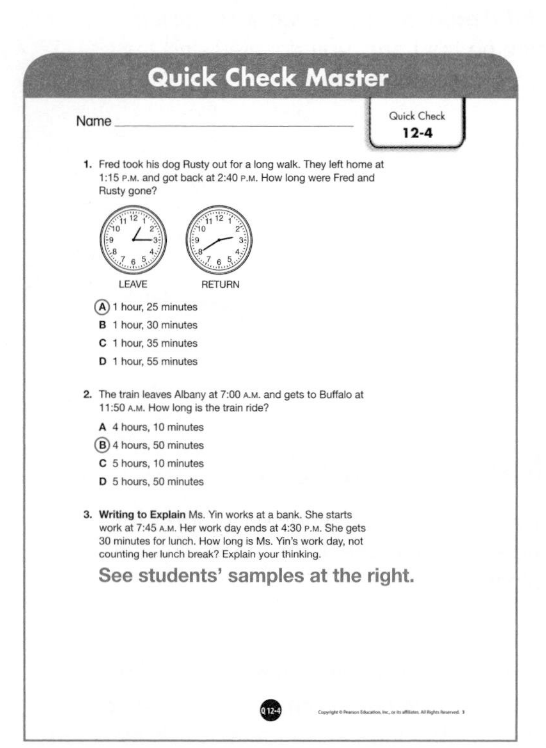

Quick Check Master

Name ____________ Quick Check 12-4

1. Fred took his dog Rusty out for a long walk. They left home at 1:15 P.M. and got back at 2:40 P.M. How long were Fred and Rusty gone?

LEAVE RETURN

(A) 1 hour, 25 minutes
B 1 hour, 30 minutes
C 1 hour, 35 minutes
D 1 hour, 55 minutes

2. The train leaves Albany at 7:00 A.M. and gets to Buffalo at 11:50 A.M. How long is the train ride?

A 4 hours, 10 minutes
(B) 4 hours, 50 minutes
C 5 hours, 10 minutes
D 5 hours, 50 minutes

3. **Writing to Explain** Ms. Yin works at a bank. She starts work at 7:45 A.M. Her work day ends at 4:30 P.M. She gets 30 minutes for lunch. How long is Ms. Yin's work day, not counting her lunch break? Explain your thinking.

See students' samples at the right.

Q12-4

Use the **Quick Check** to assess students' understanding.

Prescription for Differentiated Instruction
Use student work on the **Quick Check** to prescribe differentiated instruction.

Points	Prescription
0–3	Intervention
4	On-Level
5	Advanced

Differentiated Instruction

Intervention

Elapsed Time

 10 min 

Materials Clock face (Teaching Tool 25)

- Write this data on the chalkboard: Start time: 2:20. End time: 4:00.
- Have a student show the start time on the clock. *How much time passes from 2:20 to 3:20?* [1 hour] Show 3:20 on the clock.
- *How can you find how much time passes from 3:20 to 4:00?* [Count by fives.] Demonstrate counting by fives as you move the minute hand from 3:20 to 4:00. *How much total time has passed?* [1 hour, 40 minutes]

Practice — On-Level — Center Activity

Clip and Cover

Get Started: Get 10 squares in one color and 10 in another color, two paper clips, and two number cubes. Take turns.

At Your Turn: Toss two cubes to find your ovals. **EXAMPLE:** Choose the 3rd oval on the left and the 5th oval on the right, **or** choose the 5th oval on the left and the 3rd oval on the right. Mark your ovals with paper clips.

How to Play: The clock on the left gives the starting time. The clock on the right gives the ending time. Explain how to find the elapsed time. Cover the answer. Lose your turn if the answer is taken.

How to Win: The first player or team to get any three connected rectangles in a row or column wins.

7 hours 45 minutes	5 hours 45 minutes	7 hours 30 minutes	3 hours 30 minutes
5 hours	4 hours	2 hours 45 minutes	2 hours
3 hours 30 minutes	1 hour 15 minutes	7 hours 15 minutes	6 hours 45 minutes
9 hours	9 hours 30 minutes	5 hours 30 minutes	5 hours

If you have more time: Play again! Use your finger to trace the movement of the hour hand and minute hand on the clock as time passes.

Center Activity ★ 12-4

Practice — Advanced — Center Activity

Clip and Cover

Get Started: Get 10 squares in one color and 10 in another color, two paper clips, and two number cubes. Take turns.

At Your Turn: Toss two cubes to find your ovals. **EXAMPLE:** Choose the 3rd oval on the left and the 5th oval on the right, **or** choose the 5th oval on the left and the 3rd oval on the right. Mark your ovals with paper clips.

How to Play: The clock on the left tells the starting time. The time on the right tells the elapsed time. Explain how to find the ending time. Find and cover the answer. Lose your turn if the answer is taken.

How to Win: The first player or team to get any three connected rectangles in a row or column wins.

4 hours 30 minutes
2 hours 30 minutes
7 hours 45 minutes
3 hours 15 minutes
2 hours 30 minutes
7 hours 45 minutes

If you have more time: Play again! Talk about your strategies as you play.

Center Activity ★★ 12-4

ELL Partner Talk Listen for a strategy. For example, a student might say, "The starting time is 1:15 and the elapsed time is 2 hours and 30 minutes. I say 1:15, 2:15, 3:15, and then I add 30 minutes to get to 3:45."

Leveled Homework

Reteaching Master

Name ____________ Reteaching 12-4

Elapsed Time

A children's museum is open from 1:00 P.M. to 6:35 P.M. every day. How long is the museum open?

Step 1 Start at the starting time.

The museum is open 5 hours, 35 minutes.

Step 2 Count the hours.

There are 5 hours.

Step 3 Count the minutes.

There are 35 minutes.

Find the elapsed time.

1. Start Time: 3:30 P.M. End Time: 7:00 P.M. **3 hours, 30 minutes**
2. Start Time: 8:10 A.M. End Time: 10:55 A.M. **2 hours, 45 minutes**
3. Start Time: 1:20 P.M. End Time: 2:00 P.M. **40 minutes**
4. Start Time: 8:00 A.M. End Time: 1:15 P.M. **5 hours, 15 minutes**
5. **Write a Problem** Write the start time and the ending time of an activity that you did during the weekend. Then find the elapsed time. Write your answer in hours and minutes. **Student responses should include a starting time, an ending time, and the process they used for finding the elapsed time.**

 R 12-4

Also available in print

eTools **Time**
www.pearsonsuccessnet.com

Practice Master

Name ____________ Practice 12-4

Elapsed Time

Find the elapsed time.

1. Start Time: 6:00 P.M. End Time: 7:15 P.M. **1 hour 15 minutes**
2. Start Time: 9:30 A.M. End Time: 1:45 P.M. **4 hours 15 minutes**
3. Start Time: 3:10 P.M. End Time: 4:00 P.M. **50 minutes**
4. Start Time: 11:30 A.M. End Time: 5:30 P.M. **6 hours**
5. Start Time: 7:30 A.M. End Time: 10:50 A.M. **3 hours 20 minutes**
6. Start Time: 9:00 P.M. End Time: 4:30 A.M. **7 hours 30 minutes**
7. Edie is 1 year old. She naps from 12:45 P.M. to 2:30 P.M. each day. How long is Edie's nap? **1 hour 45 minutes**
8. Mr. Wellborn arrives at work at 8:40 A.M. He leaves for work 50 minutes before he arrives. At what times does Mr. Wellborn leave for work? **7:50 A.M.**
9. **Writing to Explain** How long is your school day? Explain how you found your answer. **Student responses should include a starting time, an ending time, and the process they used for finding the elapsed time.**
10. Gary's father dropped him off at soccer practice at 2:45 P.M. His mother picked him up at 5:00 P.M. How long did soccer practice last?
    - (A) 2 hours, 15 minutes
    - B 2 hours, 25 minutes
    - C 3 hours, 15 minutes
    - D 3 hours, 25 minutes

P 12-4

Also available in print

eTools **Time**
www.pearsonsuccessnet.com

Enrichment Master

Name ____________ Enrichment 12-4

Field Trip Planning

Your class is planning a field trip to the science museum. You have been asked to make a schedule. You need to show the start time and end time at each location you choose. The length of time the class will stay at each location is shown in the table to the right.

The trip will begin at 10:00 A.M. and will need to end by 4:30 P.M. You need to have lunch on your schedule. Leave 5 minutes between locations for time to get from one place to another place.

Location	Total Time Allowed
Animal Habitats	2 hours, 10 minutes
Bugs and Plants	1 hour, 20 minutes
Colors and Light	1 hour, 15 minutes
Electricity	30 minutes
The Human Body	2 hours, 5 minutes
Lunch Room	45 minutes
Machines and Robots	35 minutes
Ocean Life	2 hours
Surrounded by Sounds	40 minutes

Sample answer:

Field Trip Schedule

Location	Beginning Time	Ending Time
Machines and Robots	10:00	10:35
Bugs and Plants	10:40	12:00
Lunch Room	12:05	12:50
Animal Habitats	12:55	3:05
Electricity	3:10	3:40
Surrounded by Sounds	3:45	4:25

What is the total elapsed time for your field trip schedule?

Sample answer: The total elapsed time is 6 hours, 25 minutes.

 E 12-4

Also available in print

eTools **Time**
www.pearsonsuccessnet.com

Lesson
12-5

Common Core

Domain
Measurement and Data

Cluster
Solve problems involving measurement and estimation of intervals of time, liquid volumes, and masses of objects.

Standard
3.MD.1 Tell and write time to the nearest minute and measure time intervals in minutes. Solve word problems involving addition and subtraction of time intervals in minutes, e.g., by representing the problem on a number line diagram.

Mathematical Practices
- ✔ Make sense of problems and persevere in solving them.
- ○ Reason abstractly and quantitatively.
- ✔ Construct viable arguments and critique the reasoning of others.
- ✔ Model with mathematics.
- ○ Use appropriate tools strategically.
- ○ Attend to precision.
- ○ Look for and make use of structure.
- ✔ Look for and express regularity in repeated reasoning.

Problem Solving: Work Backward

Lesson Overview

Objective	Essential Understanding	Vocabulary	Materials
Students will use the strategy work backward to solve problems.	Some problems with the initial data point unknown can be solved by starting with the end result, reversing the steps and processes, and working backward to find the initial data point.		Clock face (Teaching Tool 25)

Math Background

Sometimes a problem situation gives only ending information and in-between information. Then the problem solver is asked to find the beginning information. Working backward from the given information can help the problem solver find the beginning information.

Allowing students to use manipulatives, such as clocks or money, can help them better understand the process of working backward. They can act out each step of the problem to see what has transpired.

1 Daily Common Core Review

Daily Common Core Review

Name ______ Daily Common Core Review 12-5

Choose the best answer.

1. Pablo arrives for soccer practice at the time shown on the clock below.
   At what time does Pablo arrive at soccer practice?
   A 10:43 Ⓒ 11:17
   B 11:05 D 12:43

2. What is the missing factor?
   293 × □ = 293
   A 0
   Ⓑ 1
   C 2
   D 3

3. A table has eight sides. What polygon is the tabletop?
   A Rectangle
   B Square
   C Hexagon
   Ⓓ Octagon

4. **Estimation** Big Bend National Park has about 870 Oak trees. Brazos Bend State Park has about 565 Oak trees. About how many more Oak trees does Big Bend National Park have than Brazos Bend State Park?
   Sample answer: About 300

5. There are 435 books in Sam's library. What is the value of the 3 in 435?
   30

6. There are 3 rows in the parking garage. There are 6 cars parked in each row. What is the total number of cars parked?
   18

7. What is the name of this polygon?
   Parallelogram

8. What is the name of a triangle with three equal sides?
   Equilateral triangle

D 12-5

Also available in print

Content Reviewed

Exercise 1	Time
Exercise 2	Multiplying by 1
Exercise 3	Geometry
Exercise 4	Estimate Differences
Exercise 5	Place Value
Exercise 6	Multiplication Facts
Exercise 7	Geometry
Exercise 8	Geometry

 10–15 min

Problem-Based Interactive Learning

Overview Students use pupil clock faces to solve time-related problems by working backward.

Focus How can you work backward to solve a problem?

Materials Pupil's clock face (1 per group), blank clock faces (Teaching Tool 25) (4 copies per group)

Set the Purpose *You know that some events happen before other events. Today, you will work backward to solve a time problem.*

Connect *Have you ever had to make a schedule? How did you figure out how much time to allow for each activity on your schedule?* [Sample response: I estimated about how long each activity would take, chose times, and checked if they worked.]

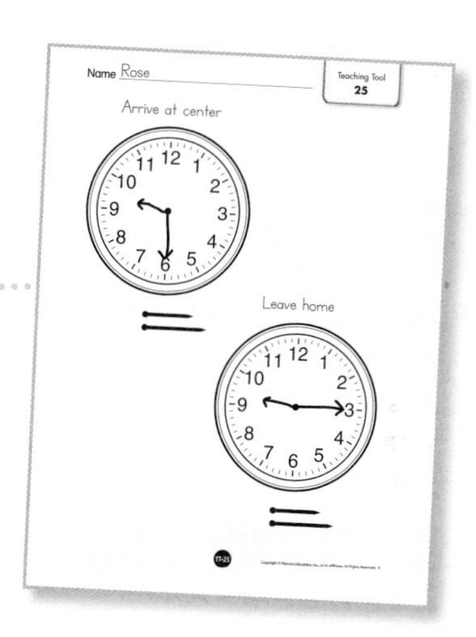

Model with Mathematics
Have students use a clock face to model the starting time and ending time for each event.

Pose the Problem *Nina wants to arrive at the community center at 9:30 A.M. for an art class. It takes her 15 minutes to walk to the center, 15 minutes to get ready, and 30 minutes to make and eat breakfast. What time should she start making breakfast? Use your clock face to solve the problem by working backward. Record each time on Teaching Tool 25.*

Whole-Class Discussion *What information were you given to help you solve the problem?* [How much time each activity takes, and the time Nina wants to arrive for the class] *What were you asked to find?* [The time Nina should start making breakfast] Discuss students' solutions and methods. Highlight the strategy of working backward. *What is the order of events in this problem?* [Nina makes and eats breakfast, gets ready, then walks to class by 9:30.] *It takes 15 minutes for Nina to walk, so what time should she leave home?* [9:15] *How is this working backward?* [You work backward from the arrival time.] With the class, continue working backward to solve. Also show the backward movement of the hands on a pupil clock face. Nina should start making breakfast at 8:30 A.M.

Small-Group Interaction Allow students to work in pairs to solve the following problem. *School starts at 8:15 A.M. It takes Hal 15 minutes to walk to school, 20 minutes to eat, and 25 minutes to get ready. What time should he get up?* [7:15 A.M.]

You know it takes 2 hours to get from Northville to Southville by train. You know what time Lily arrives at Southville. Write a word problem to figure out what time Lily's train left Northville. Have a partner solve your problem and draw clocks showing the times. [Answers will vary.]

3 Develop the Concept: Visual

Visual Learning

Problem Solving

Work Backward

Eric's family wants to arrive at the movie theater at 2:30 P.M. It takes them 30 minutes to travel to the theater, 15 minutes to get ready, and 30 minutes to eat lunch. What time should the family start eating lunch?

Arrive at Theater

What does the picture of the clock show about the problem? [It shows the time Eric's family wants to arrive at the movie theater.]

Read and Understand

What do I know?	Arrive 2:30 P.M., 30 minutes to travel, 15 minutes to get ready, 30 minutes to eat lunch
What am I being asked to find?	The time the family should start eating lunch

1 Visual Learning

Set the Purpose Call students' attention to the **Visual Learning Bridge** at the top of the page. *In this lesson you will learn to work backward from given information to solve a problem.*

2 Guided Practice

MATHEMATICAL PRACTICES

Remind students to identify and begin working backward from the ending information.

Exercise 3
Error Intervention

If students have difficulty writing a problem that can be solved by working backward,

then ask: *How can writing a problem that requires working forward help you write a problem that requires working backward?* [You can write a problem that requires working forward and solve it. Then you can remove the beginning information and ask the solver to find it.]

Reteaching Show students how to draw a picture and work backward to solve the following problem: When Jake left the movie, he had $14 in his pocket. At the movie, Jake paid $2.50 for a drink, $3.25 for popcorn, and $5.25 for his ticket. How much money did Jake have before he went to the movie? [$25] For another example and more practice, assign **Reteaching** Set E on p. 317.

3 Independent Practice

MATHEMATICAL PRACTICES

The problem-solving strategy ***Work Backward*** can be helpful in trying to solve problems with ending information. To review this strategy, refer students to the Problem-Solving Handbook.

Lesson 12-5

Common Core

3.MD.1 Tell and write time to the nearest minute and measure time intervals in minutes. Solve word problems involving addition and subtraction of time intervals in minutes, e.g., by representing the problem on a number line diagram.

Problem Solving

Work Backward

Eric's family wants to arrive at the movie theater at 2:30 P.M. It takes them 30 minutes to travel to the theater, 15 minutes to get ready, and 30 minutes to eat lunch. What time should the family start eating lunch?

Arrive at Theater

Guided Practice*

MATHEMATICAL PRACTICES

Do you know HOW?

Solve the problem by drawing a picture and working backward.
Pictures will vary.

1. The swim meet starts at 10:15 A.M. It takes Abby 15 minutes to walk to the pool. On her way, she needs 15 minutes to shop. It takes her 30 minutes to get ready. What time should Abby start getting ready?
9:15 A.M.

Do you UNDERSTAND?

2. In the example above, why do the arrows in the Solve step move to the left?
See margin.

3. **Write a Problem** Write a problem that you can solve by working backward.
Answers will vary.

Independent Practice

MATHEMATICAL PRACTICES

Persevere In **4** and **5**, solve the problem by drawing a picture and working backward. Pictures will vary.

4. Emilio read the thermometer one evening. The temperature was 56°F. This temperature was 9°F less than the temperature that afternoon. The afternoon temperature was 7°F greater than the temperature in the morning. What was the temperature in the morning?
58°F

5. Jana's dentist appointment is at 4:30 P.M. It takes Jana 20 minutes to walk to the dentist's office, 20 minutes to get ready, and 30 minutes to clean her room. What time should she start cleaning her room?
3:20 P.M.

Applying Math Practices

- What am I asked to find?
- What else can I try?
- How are quantities related?
- How can I explain my work?
- How can I use math to model the problem?
- Can I use tools to help?
- Is my work precise?
- Why does this work?
- How can I generalize?

*For another example, see Set E on page 317.

Answer

2. You are counting backward to an earlier time for each activity.

Visual Learning Animation

www.pearsonsuccessnet.com or CD

What is the order of the activities the family needs to do? [Eat lunch, get ready, travel, arrive]

Plan and Solve

Draw a picture to show each change.

Eat 30 min, Get Ready 15 min, Travel 30 min; Start Eating ?; Arrive 2:30 P.M.

Work backward from the end.

Start Eating 1:15 P.M. −30 min 1:45 P.M. −15 min 2:00 P.M. −30 min Arrive 2:30 P.M.

Eric's family should start eating lunch at 1:15 P.M.

What math operation can you use when working backward to find a time? [Subtraction]

Read and Understand

What do I know?	Arrive 2:30 P.M., 30 minutes to travel, 15 minutes to get ready, 30 minutes to eat lunch
What am I being asked to find?	The time the family should start eating lunch

Plan and Solve

Draw a picture to show each change.

Eat 30 min, Get Ready 15 min, Travel 30 min; Start Eating ?; Arrive 2:30 P.M.

Work backward from the end.

Start Eating 1:15 P.M. −30 min 1:45 P.M. −15 min 2:00 P.M. −30 min Arrive 2:30 P.M.

Eric's family should start eating lunch at 1:15 P.M.

6. **Model** Use the number line above. Eric's family decides to clean their garage before eating lunch. It will take them 45 minutes to clean. They still plan to arrive at the movie theater at 2:30 P.M. What time should they start cleaning the garage?
   12:30 P.M.

7. **Model** Lisa has soccer practice at 3:45 P.M. It takes her 10 minutes to warm up and 15 minutes to get from home to practice. What time should Lisa leave home to get to practice on time? Draw a number line to model the problem.
   See margin.

8. **Generalize** Wan-li drew these polygons. What is the same in all three polygons?

Each has one right angle.

9. School starts at 8:15 A.M. It takes Shane 15 minutes to walk to school, 20 minutes to eat, 15 minutes to walk his dog, and 15 minutes to get ready. What time should he get up?
   7:10 A.M.

10. A scientist recorded the data shown in the table. About how long does it take a Venus Flytrap to close after an insect or spider lands on it?
    (A) Less than 1 second
    B More than 1 second
    C More than 1 minute
    D More than 2 minutes

Time Prey Landed	Time Flytrap Closed
2:07	$\frac{1}{2}$ second after 2:07
2:49	$\frac{3}{4}$ second after 2:49
2:53	$\frac{1}{2}$ second after 2:53

Lesson 12-5 315

Students use underlying processes and mathematical tools for Exercises 4–10. Remind students to check for reasonableness when solving each problem.

Exercises 5 and 9
Some students may solve the problem by adding up the time it takes to perform all the tasks and then subtracting that amount of time from the ending time. Encourage this type of thinking.

Exercise 6
Model with Mathematics Encourage students to copy and extend the number line shown in the visual learning bridge. Students' number lines should include the time Eric's family wants to begin cleaning the garage. ***How can you work backward on your number line to show the time Eric's family should begin cleaning the garage?*** [Continue working backward from the time the family starts eating and subtract 45 minutes from 1:15 P.M. Then label the new start time and event on the number line.]

Exercise 7
Model with Mathematics Encourage students to refer to the number line model shown in the visual learning bridge as they begin constructing their own number lines for this exercise. They can start by labeling the end event and time. ***What ending event and time can be shown on your number line?*** [Soccer practice; 3:45 P.M.]

Exercise 8
Make Generalizations Some students may have difficulty identifying what is the same in the polygons. Encourage students to look at various characteristics of the polygons, for example, the number of sides, the lengths of the sides, and the types of angles, to find the answer.

7. 3:20 P.M. Leaves Home —(−15 min)— 3:35 P.M. —(−10 min)— 3:45 P.M. Arrives

4 Close/Assess and Differentiate

Close

Essential Understanding Some problems with the initial data point unknown can be solved by starting with the end result, reversing the steps and processes and working backward to find the initial data point. ***In this lesson you learned how to work backward from given information to solve a problem.***

Exercises 1 and 2 are worth 1 point each.
Use the rubric to score Exercise 3.

Exercise 3

Writing to Explain Students should combine the strategies of drawing a picture and working backwards to solve a problem about temperatures that change over time.

ELL Suggest a Sequence Encourage students to use the following words in their response: *first, then, next, finally*.

Student Samples

3-point answer The student answers correctly, and provides a thorough explanation and a useful picture.

I drew a number line to stand for the thermometer. I circled 21 for the temperature at noon. I jumped back 7 to find the temperature at 8:00 A.M. I jumped back 4 from 21 for the temperature at 6:00 P.M. I labeled each temperature with the time it was then. The picture shows that it was 3°C cooler at 8:00 A.M. than it was at 6:00 P.M.

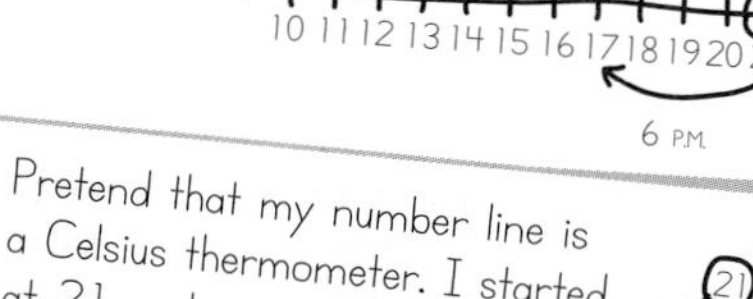

2-point answer The student answers correctly and provides an adequate explanation and picture.

Pretend that my number line is a Celsius thermometer. I started at 21 and moved back 7 to stand for getting cooler. That put me at 14. I jumped back 4 from 21 (cooler). That put me at 17. I saw that it was 3 degrees cooler at 8 A.M. than at 6 P.M.

1-point answer The student answers correctly with or without a picture, and with no explanation.

It was 3 degrees cooler at 8:00 A.M. than it was at 6:00 P.M.

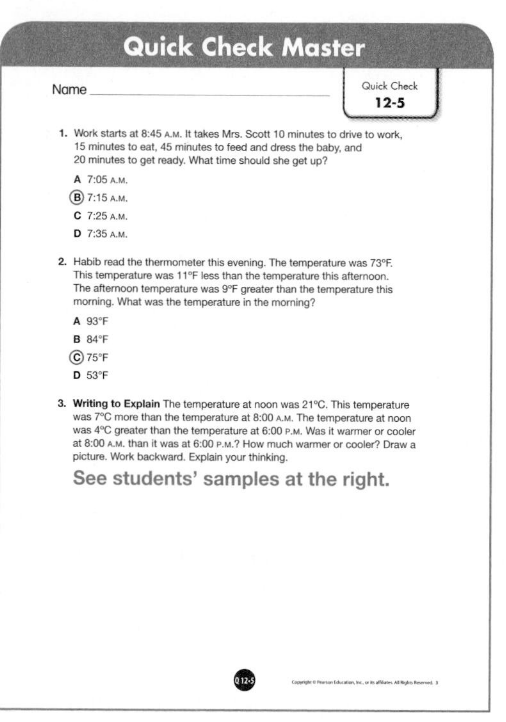

Quick Check Master

Name ______ Quick Check 12-5

1. Work starts at 8:45 A.M. It takes Mrs. Scott 10 minutes to drive to work, 15 minutes to eat, 45 minutes to feed and dress the baby, and 20 minutes to get ready. What time should she get up?
   A 7:05 A.M.
   (B) 7:15 A.M.
   C 7:25 A.M.
   D 7:35 A.M.
2. Habib read the thermometer this evening. The temperature was 73°F. This temperature was 11°F less than the temperature this afternoon. The afternoon temperature was 9°F greater than the temperature this morning. What was the temperature in the morning?
   A 93°F
   B 84°F
   (C) 75°F
   D 53°F
3. **Writing to Explain** The temperature at noon was 21°C. This temperature was 7°C more than the temperature at 8:00 A.M. The temperature at noon was 4°C greater than the temperature at 6:00 P.M. Was it warmer or cooler at 8:00 A.M. than it was at 6:00 P.M.? How much warmer or cooler? Draw a picture. Work backward. Explain your thinking.
   See students' samples at the right.

Formative Assessment

Use the **Quick Check** to assess students' understanding.

Prescription for Differentiated Instruction

Use student work on the **Quick Check** to prescribe differentiated instruction.

Points	Prescription
0–3	Intervention
4	On-Level
5	Advanced

Differentiated Instruction

Intervention

One Step Back at a Time

 15 min 

- Give students this problem: Sarah spent $25 on a sweater. She had $20 left over. How much money did she have before she bought the sweater?
- Ask students to identify the operation they would use and to solve the problem.
- Add another step to the problem: Sarah withdrew $40 from the bank before she went shopping. How much money did she have before she went to the bank?
- Ask students to identify the operation and solve the next step of the problem.
- Try some one- and then two-step problems with time and temperature.

Practice — On-Level — Center Activity

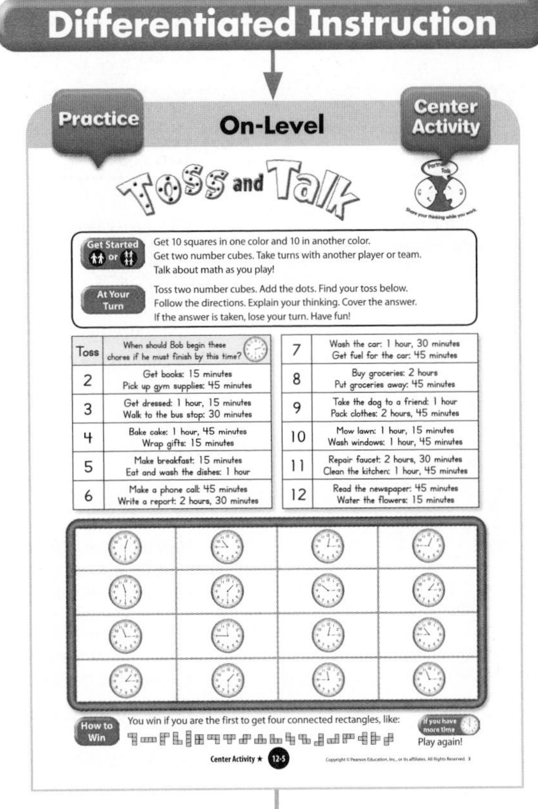

Toss and Talk

Get Started Get 10 squares in one color and 10 in another color. Get two number cubes. Take turns with another player or team. Talk about math as you play!

At Your Turn Toss two number cubes. Add the dots. Find your toss below. Follow the directions. Explain your thinking. Cover the answer. If the answer is taken, lose your turn. Have fun!

Toss	When should Bob begin these chores if he must finish by this time?
2	Get books: 15 minutes Pick up gym supplies: 45 minutes
3	Get dressed: 1 hour, 15 minutes Walk to the bus stop: 30 minutes
4	Bake cake: 1 hour, 45 minutes Wrap gifts: 15 minutes
5	Make breakfast: 15 minutes Eat and wash the dishes: 1 hour
6	Make a phone call: 45 minutes Write a report: 2 hours, 30 minutes
7	Wash the car: 1 hour, 30 minutes Get fuel for the car: 45 minutes
8	Buy groceries: 2 hours Put groceries away: 45 minutes
9	Take the dog to a friend: 1 hour Pack clothes: 2 hours, 45 minutes
10	Mow lawn: 1 hour, 15 minutes Wash windows: 1 hour, 45 minutes
11	Repair faucet: 2 hours, 30 minutes Clean the kitchen: 1 hour, 45 minutes
12	Read the newspaper: 45 minutes Water the flowers: 15 minutes

How to Win You win if you are the first to get four connected rectangles, like:

If you have more time: Play again!

Center Activity ★ 12-5

Practice — Advanced — Center Activity

Toss and Talk

Get Started Get 10 squares in one color and 10 in another color. Get two number cubes. Take turns with another player or team. Talk about math as you play!

At Your Turn Toss two number cubes. Add the dots. Find your toss below. Follow the directions. Explain your thinking. Cover the answer. If the answer is taken, lose your turn. Have fun!

Toss	What time should Sue start these activities if she must finish at the time shown?
2	Exercise: 2 h, 15 min Get car washed: 45 minutes
3	Make phone calls: 30 min Write a report: 1 h, 15 min
4	Clean room: 45 min Call friend: 30 min
5	Bake cake: 1 h, 30 min Set table: 15 min
6	Feed cats: 30 min Read newspaper: 45 min
7	Make sandwiches: 1 h, 45 min Pack picnic: 45 min
8	Visit friend: 1 h, 15 min Walk home: 45 min
9	Make and eat dinner: 2 h Take a walk: 15 min
10	Plan party: 1 h, 15 min Buy presents: 2 h
11	Go to softball game: 1 h, 15 min Get dressed: 15 min
12	Pick clothes: 30 min Get dressed: 45 min

How to Win You win if you are the first to get four connected rectangles, like:

If you have more time: Play again!

Center Activity ★★ 12-5

ELL Partner Talk To check understanding, ask a student to repeat and complete this sentence: ***If one chore takes 15 minutes and another chore takes 1 hour, and the chores have to be completed by 2:30, then we should start the chores at or before ___.*** [1:15]

Leveled Homework

Reteaching Master

Name __________ Reteaching 12-5

Problem Solving: Work Backward

Natalie finished listening to music at 4:30 P.M. She had listened to a CD that lasted 40 minutes. She spent 15 minutes listening to radio music after the CD finished. Then she listened to another CD for 45 minutes. At what time did Natalie start listening to music?

You can work backward to solve problems. Use each piece of information to find the starting time.

Natalie finished listening to music at 4:30 P.M.

She listened to the second CD for 45 minutes.	45 minutes before 4:30 P.M. is 3:45 P.M.	
She spent 15 minutes listening to radio music.	15 minutes from 3:45 P.M. is 3:30 P.M.	
She listened to the first CD for 40 minutes.	40 minutes before 3:30 P.M. is 2:50 P.M.	

Natalie started listening to music at 2:50 P.M.

Solve the problem by drawing a picture and working backward.

1. The temperature at 6 P.M. was 72°F. This temperature was 8°F less than at 4 P.M. The temperature at 10 A.M. was 5°F greater than the 4 P.M. temperature. What was the temperature at 10 A.M.? **85°F**

R 12-5

Also available in print

DIGITAL eTools **Time**
www.pearsonsuccessnet.com

Practice Master

Name __________ Practice 12-5

Problem Solving: Work Backward

Solve the problem by drawing a picture or a number line and working backward.

1. Will arrived at his mother's office at 3 P.M. It took him 30 minutes to walk from his home to the mall. He was in the mall for 45 minutes. It then took him 15 minutes to walk to his mother's office. At what time did Will leave home? **1:30 P.M.**
2. At 12 noon, Leslie recorded the temperature as 56°F. The temperature had increased by 8°F from 10 A.M. The temperature at 8 A.M. was 2°F warmer than it was at 10 A.M. What was the temperature at 8 A.M.? **50°F**
3. The test that Keyshawn's class took finished at 10:30 A.M. The first part of the test took 30 minutes. There was a 15-minute break. The second part of the test also took 30 minutes. At what time did the test start? **9:15 A.M.**
4. The temperature was 16°C when Becky returned home at 6 P.M. The temperature was 4°C warmer at 3 P.M. than it was at 6 P.M. It was 3°C warmer at 12 noon than it was at 3 P.M. What was the temperature at 12 noon? **23°C**
5. Elliot finished studying at 4:45 P.M. He spent 30 minutes reading a social studies chapter. He spent 45 minutes on his math homework. In between studying, Elliot took a 20-minute break. At what time did Elliot begin studying?

   A 3:00 P.M. (B) 3:10 P.M. C 3:30 P.M. D 6:20 P.M.

   Check student drawings or number lines.

P 12-5

Also available in print

DIGITAL eTools **Time**
www.pearsonsuccessnet.com

Enrichment Master

Name __________ Enrichment 12-5

Find the Way Back

1. Peter started at the corner of Broad and High Street. He walked 2 blocks north, turned left and walked 4 blocks, turned right, and walked 1 block. Using the same path, how can Peter get back to Broad and High? **1 block south, turn left, walk 4 blocks, turn right, walk 2 blocks**
2. Blaine drove to Molly's house. He drove 1 mile west, then 5 miles north, and 1 mile east. How can Blaine drive home from Molly's house using the same path? **1 mi west, 5 mi south, and 1 mi east**
3. Marshall left his house by car. He drove 3 miles north, turned west and drove twice as far. He turned south and drove 1 more mile. Tell Marshall how to return home using the same path. **1 mi north, 6 mi east, 3 mi south**
4. Sally hiked part of the Appalachian Trail, starting at Katahdin, Maine. She went 2 kilometers east, 4 kilometers south, and 1 kilometer west. How can Sally return to Katahdin using the same path? **1 km east, 4 km north, and 2 km west**
5. Joshua ran in a city marathon. He ran 8 miles south, 12 miles east, 3 miles south, and 3 miles west. His friend, Tom, was waiting for him at the finish line with a car. Tom wants to drive the same route back. Tell Tom how to drive back to the starting line using the same path. **3 mi east, 3 mi north, 12 mi west, and 8 mi north**

E 12-5

Also available in print

DIGITAL eTools **Time**
www.pearsonsuccessnet.com

Time
RETEACHING

Set A, pages 304–306

The clocks show the time that a movie starts. What time does the movie start? Write the time in at least 3 ways.

When the minute hand is on the 9, you can say "15 minutes to" the hour. You can also say "a quarter to" the hour.

The movie starts at four forty-five, or 15 minutes to five, or a quarter to five.

Remember to find where the hour hand points and where the minute hand points to tell the time.

Write the time shown on each clock in two ways. Sample answers are given.

1. 6:45 six forty-five; 15 minutes to seven; a quarter to seven
2.  15 minutes past eight; a quarter past eight; 8:15

Set B, pages 308–309

What is the time to the nearest minute?

The hour hand is between 10 and 11. The time is after 10:00.

Count by 5s from the 12 to the 5.
5, 10, 15, 20, 25 minutes.

After counting by 5s, count the marks by 1.
5, 10, 15, 20, 25, 26, 27 minutes.

The digital time is 10:27.
It is 27 minutes past 10 or 33 minutes to 11.

Remember that for minutes, count numbers on the clock by 5s, then count marks by 1.

Write the time shown on each clock in two ways. Sample answers are given.

1. 12:17; 17 minutes past 12
2. 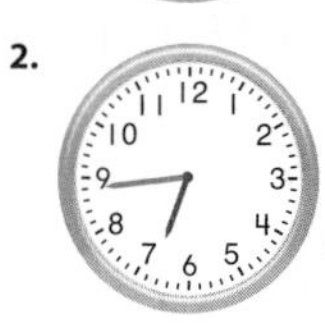 44 minutes past 6; 16 minutes to 7

Set C, pages 310–311

Change 9 weeks to days.

9 weeks = ☐ days
Change to days.

You know that 1 week equals 7 days.

Multiply: 9 × 7 days = 63 days

9 weeks = 63 days

Remember to use the correct factors for the units you are changing.

1. 6 hours = ☐ minutes 360
2. 2 weeks = ☐ days 14
3. 3 days = ☐ hours 72
4. 1 hour, 41 minutes = ☐ minutes 101
5. 2 days, 3 hours = ☐ hours 51
6. 3 hours, 15 minutes = ☐ minutes 195

Set D, pages 312–313

How long does the hockey game last?
Start Time: 11:00 A.M.
End Time: 2:35 P.M.

- Find the starting time: **11:00 A.M.**
- Count the hours: **12, 1, 2.**
- Count the minutes: **5, 10, 15, 20, 25, 30, 35.**

The game lasted 3 hours, 35 minutes.

Remember to count hours and then minutes.

Find the elapsed time.

1. Start Time: 9:00 A.M.
   End Time: 12:15 P.M.
   3 hours, 15 minutes
2. Start Time: 5:00 P.M.
   End Time: 9:50 P.M.
   4 hours, 50 minutes

Set E, pages 314–315

Jay's soccer practice begins at 10:00 A.M. He takes 30 minutes to walk to the field. He takes 10 minutes to walk his dog and 10 minutes to get ready. When should Jay start getting ready?

Work backward from the end using the opposite of each change.

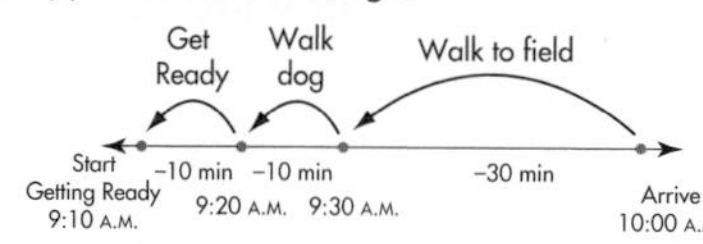

Jay should start getting ready at 9:10 A.M.

Remember to check your solution by working forward.

Solve by drawing a picture and working backward.

1. Hal needs to meet Lou at 1:00 P.M. It takes him 10 minutes to walk to Lou's house, 10 minutes to get ready, and 20 minutes to eat lunch. What time should Hal start eating lunch? 12:20 P.M.

Purpose

- Provide students with more examples and practice for each lesson in the topic.
- For intervention materials, use the resources listed in the chart on the following page.

Response to Intervention

Ongoing Intervention

- Lessons with guiding questions to assess understanding
- Support to prevent misconceptions and to reteach

Strategic Intervention

- Targeted to small groups who need more support
- Easy to implement

Intensive Intervention

- Instruction to accelerate progress
- Instruction focused on foundational skills

Item Analysis for Diagnosis and Intervention

Objective	Common Core Standards	Reteaching Sets	Student Book Lessons	Intervention System
Tell and write time to the half hour and quarter hour.	**3.MD.1**	Set A, 1–2	12-1	D13
Tell and write time to the minute.	**3.MD.1**	Set B, 1–2	12-2	D14
Solve simple unit of time conversions.	**3.MD.1**	Set C, 1–6	12-3	D15
Find the elapsed time between two events.	**3.MD.1**	Set D, 1–2	12-4	D16
Work backward to solve problems.	**3.MD.1**	Set E, 1	12-5	E30

TOPIC TEST

Topic 12 Test

ASSESSMENT

Multiple Choice

1. The clock below shows the time Levi arrived at the doctor's office. What time did he arrive? (12-2)

A 3:42
(B) 3:37
C 3:35
D 2:37

2. What is one way to write the time shown on the clock? (12-1)

A Quarter to 1
B 15 past 1
C Quarter past 2
(D) Quarter to 2

3. Anita got to school at 8:05 A.M. She was on the bus 15 minutes, stood at the bus stop for 10 minutes, and took 40 minutes to get ready after she got up. What time did Anita get up? (12-5)

A 9:10 A.M.
B 7:05 A.M.
(C) 7:00 A.M.
D 6:55 A.M.

4. Brad is going on vacation for 2 weeks. Which amount of time is greater than 2 weeks? (12-3)

A 5 days
B 7 days
C 14 days
(D) 18 days

5. Linda left her house at 12:40 P.M. She spent 15 minutes driving to the deli, 5 minutes waiting in line, and then 20 minutes eating her lunch. What time did she finish her lunch? (12-4)

A 12:55 P.M.
B 1:15 P.M.
(C) 1:20 P.M.
D 1:40 P.M.

6. Which of the following is a time that Jose would be asleep during the night? (12-1)

A 3:15 P.M.
(B) 11:45 P.M.
C 10:45 A.M.
D 12:30 P.M.

7. It was 3:00 P.M. Sandra had been at the bus station for 45 minutes. When did she arrive at the station? (12-4)

(A) 2:15 P.M.
B 2:30 P.M.
C 3:15 P.M.
D 3:45 P.M.

318

Constructed Response

8. Judy says that she planted an apple seed 3 days ago. Her brother thinks she planted the seed less than 40 hours ago. Is Judy's brother correct? Explain your answer. (12-3) See Below.

9. Jon arrived home from school at the time shown on the clock.

What time did Jon arrive? (12-2) 3:24

10. Olivia left her house at 6:30 to go to the movies. What is another way to write 6:30? (12-1) Sample answer: half past 6 or six thirty

11. The Brown family boarded a train at 3:55 P.M. to go home from the county fair. It took them 25 minutes to get to the train station from the fair. They spent 1 hour, 15 minutes, at the fair. What time did they arrive at the fair? Draw a number line to model the problem. (12-5) See margin.

12. The concert in the park started at 11:15 A.M. and ended at 1:50 P.M. How long did the concert last? (12-4) 2 hours, 35 minutes

13. How many hours are in 4 days? (12-3) 96

8. No; 3 days = 72 hours which is greater than 40 hours.

14. The 3:00 P.M. temperature was 93°F. This was 8° warmer than the temperature at noon. The noon temperature was 13° warmer than the 9:00 A.M. temperature. What was the 9:00 A.M. temperature in °F? (12-5) 72° F

15. Jen was playing in a soccer game. The game started at 11:10 A.M. and ended at 12:40 P.M. How long did the game last? (12-4) 1 hour, 30 minutes

16. Reading hour at the library starts at the time shown on the clock. What time does reading hour begin? (12-1) 1:15

17. The game ended at 5:15 P.M. It lasted 2 hours 10 minutes. What time did the game start? (12-4) 3:05 P.M.

18. Dan and his mom are going to a baseball game that starts at 7:05 P.M. Batting practice starts 90 minutes before the game starts. It takes 45 minutes for them to get to the ballpark. What time do Dan and his mom need to leave to see the start of batting practice? (12-5) 4:50 P.M.

Topic 12 Test 319

Purpose

- Assess students' understanding of the concepts and skills in Topic 12 using multiple-choice and constructed response formats.
- Additional assessment options can be found in the Teacher Resource Masters.
- For intervention materials that correspond to the multiple-choice test, use the resources listed in the chart on the following page.

11. They arrived at 2:15 P.M.

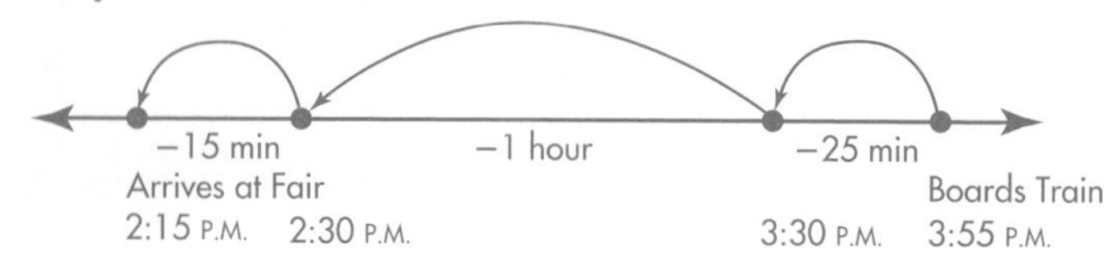

Test-Taking Tips

Discuss with students the following tips for test success.

Understand the Question
- Look for important words.
- Turn the question into a statement: "I need to find out ..."

Gather the Information
- Get information from text.
- Get information from pictures, maps, diagrams, tables, and graphs.

Make a Plan
- Think about problem-solving skills and strategies.
- Choose computation methods.

Make Smart Choices
- Eliminate wrong answers.
- Try working backward from an answer.
- Check answers for reasonableness; estimate.

Item Analysis for Diagnosis and Intervention

Objective	Common Core Standards	Test Items	Student Book Lessons	Intervention System
Tell and write time to the half and quarter hour.	**3.MD.1**	2, 6, 10, 16	12-1	D13
Tell and write time to the minute.	**3.MD.1**	1, 9	12-2	D14
Convert units of time.	**3.MD.1**	4, 8, 13	12-3	D15
Find elapsed time.	**3.MD.1**	5, 7, 12, 15, 17	12-4	D16
Work backward to solve problems.	**3.MD.1**	3, 11, 14, 18	12-5	E30

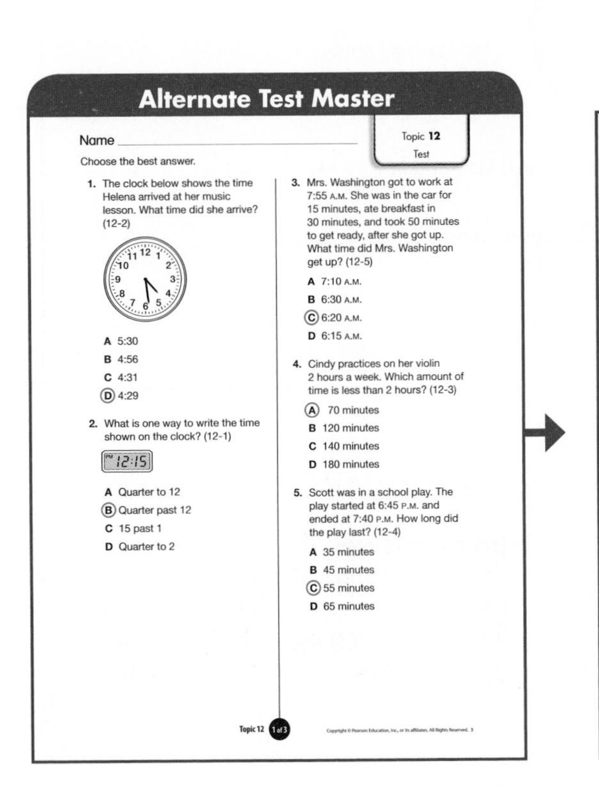

Alternate Test Master

Name ____________ Topic 12 Test

Choose the best answer.

1. The clock below shows the time Helena arrived at her music lesson. What time did she arrive? (12-2)
   A 5:30
   B 4:56
   C 4:31
   (D) 4:29

2. What is one way to write the time shown on the clock? (12-1) 12:15
   A Quarter to 12
   (B) Quarter past 12
   C 15 past 1
   D Quarter to 2

3. Mrs. Washington got to work at 7:55 A.M. She was in the car for 15 minutes, ate breakfast in 30 minutes, and took 50 minutes to get ready, after she got up. What time did Mrs. Washington get up? (12-5)
   A 7:10 A.M.
   B 6:30 A.M.
   (C) 6:20 A.M.
   D 6:15 A.M.

4. Cindy practices on her violin 2 hours a week. Which amount of time is less than 2 hours? (12-3)
   (A) 70 minutes
   B 120 minutes
   C 140 minutes
   D 180 minutes

5. Scott was in a school play. The play started at 6:45 P.M. and ended at 7:40 P.M. How long did the play last? (12-4)
   A 35 minutes
   B 45 minutes
   (C) 55 minutes
   D 65 minutes

Topic 12 1 of 3

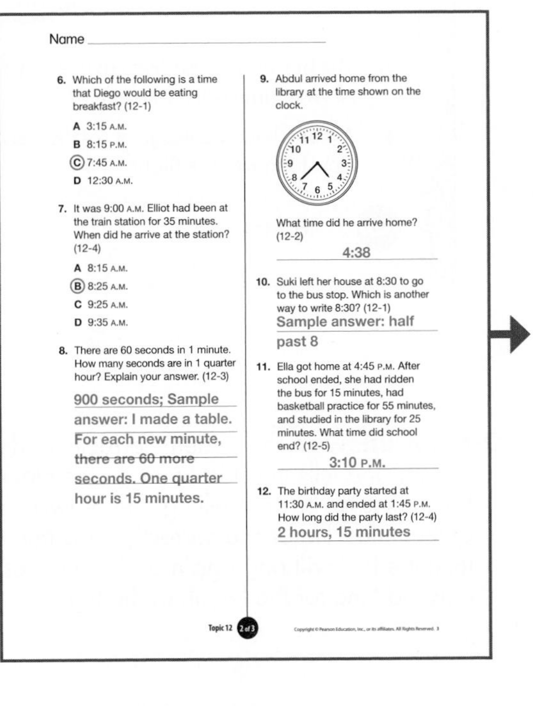

Name ____________

6. Which of the following is a time that Diego would be eating breakfast? (12-1)
   A 3:15 A.M.
   B 8:15 P.M.
   (C) 7:45 A.M.
   D 12:30 A.M.

7. It was 9:00 A.M. Elliot had been at the train station for 35 minutes. When did he arrive at the station? (12-4)
   A 8:15 A.M.
   (B) 8:25 A.M.
   C 9:25 A.M.
   D 9:35 A.M.

8. There are 60 seconds in 1 minute. How many seconds are in 1 quarter hour? Explain your answer. (12-3)
   900 seconds; Sample answer: I made a table. For each new minute, there are 60 more seconds. One quarter hour is 15 minutes.

9. Abdul arrived home from the library at the time shown on the clock.
   What time did he arrive home? (12-2)
   4:38

10. Suki left her house at 8:30 to go to the bus stop. Which is another way to write 8:30? (12-1)
    Sample answer: half past 8

11. Ella got home at 4:45 P.M. After school ended, she had ridden the bus for 15 minutes, had basketball practice for 55 minutes, and studied in the library for 25 minutes. What time did school end? (12-5)
    3:10 P.M.

12. The birthday party started at 11:30 A.M. and ended at 1:45 P.M. How long did the party last? (12-4)
    2 hours, 15 minutes

Topic 12 2 of 3

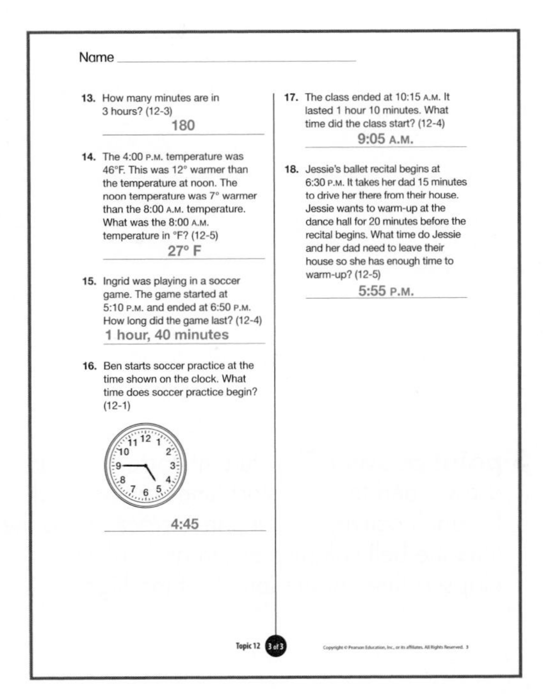

Name ____________

13. How many minutes are in 3 hours? (12-3)
    180

14. The 4:00 P.M. temperature was 46°F. This was 12° warmer than the temperature at noon. The noon temperature was 7° warmer than the 8:00 A.M. temperature. What was the 8:00 A.M. temperature in °F? (12-5)
    27° F

15. Ingrid was playing in a soccer game. The game started at 5:10 P.M. and ended at 6:50 P.M. How long did the game last? (12-4)
    1 hour, 40 minutes

16. Ben starts soccer practice at the time shown on the clock. What time does soccer practice begin? (12-1)
    4:45

17. The class ended at 10:15 A.M. It lasted 1 hour 10 minutes. What time did the class start? (12-4)
    9:05 A.M.

18. Jessie's ballet recital begins at 6:30 P.M. It takes her dad 15 minutes to drive her there from their house. Jessie wants to warm-up at the dance hall for 20 minutes before the recital begins. What time do Jessie and her dad need to leave their house so she has enough time to warm-up? (12-5)
    5:55 P.M.

Topic 12 3 of 3

PERFORMANCE ASSESSMENT

Purpose Assess students' understanding of the concepts and skills in Topic 12 through a performance-based task.

Task For this assessment, students work backward from the end time to find start times. Also, they find elapsed time.

Get Ready Use a clock face to review how to work backward from the end time to find a start time. Have students state each time in two ways. Also practice finding elapsed time given a start time and an end time.

Guiding the Activity Encourage students to check their work by working forward from their answer to the end time.

Questioning Strategies How can you count minutes backward? How do you say the time after an hour? How long did the event last in hours and minutes?

You need to arrive at the theater at exactly 12:15 P.M. for a movie. It takes you 30 minutes to walk to the theater, 40 minutes to get ready, and 30 minutes to walk your dog.

1. Write the time you should start each activity in two ways.

Arrive at theater  12:15 P.M. a quarter after twelve

Start walking to theater  11:45 A.M. a quarter before twelve

Start getting ready  11:05 A.M. five after eleven

Start walking dog  10:35 A.M. thirty-five after 10

2. The bell rings at Addison gym every half hour. It last rang at 7:12 A.M. At what time will it ring again? 7:42 A.M.

3. A plane leaves Chicago at 6:45 P.M. and arrives in Kansas City at 8:10 P.M. How long was the flight? 1 hour, 25 minutes

320 Topic 12

Scoring Rubric

3-point answer The student correctly finds, draws, and tells the start times on the clock for each activity. He or she correctly finds the time the bell will ring again and calculates elapsed time for the length of the flight.

2-point answer The student correctly finds, draws, and tells the start times on the clock but makes an error in telling one or two of the times. He or she correctly finds the time the bell will ring again and calculates elapsed time for the length of the flight.

1-point answer The student has trouble drawing and telling several of the start times. He or she may find the time when the bell will ring again but is not able to give the elapsed time for the flight.

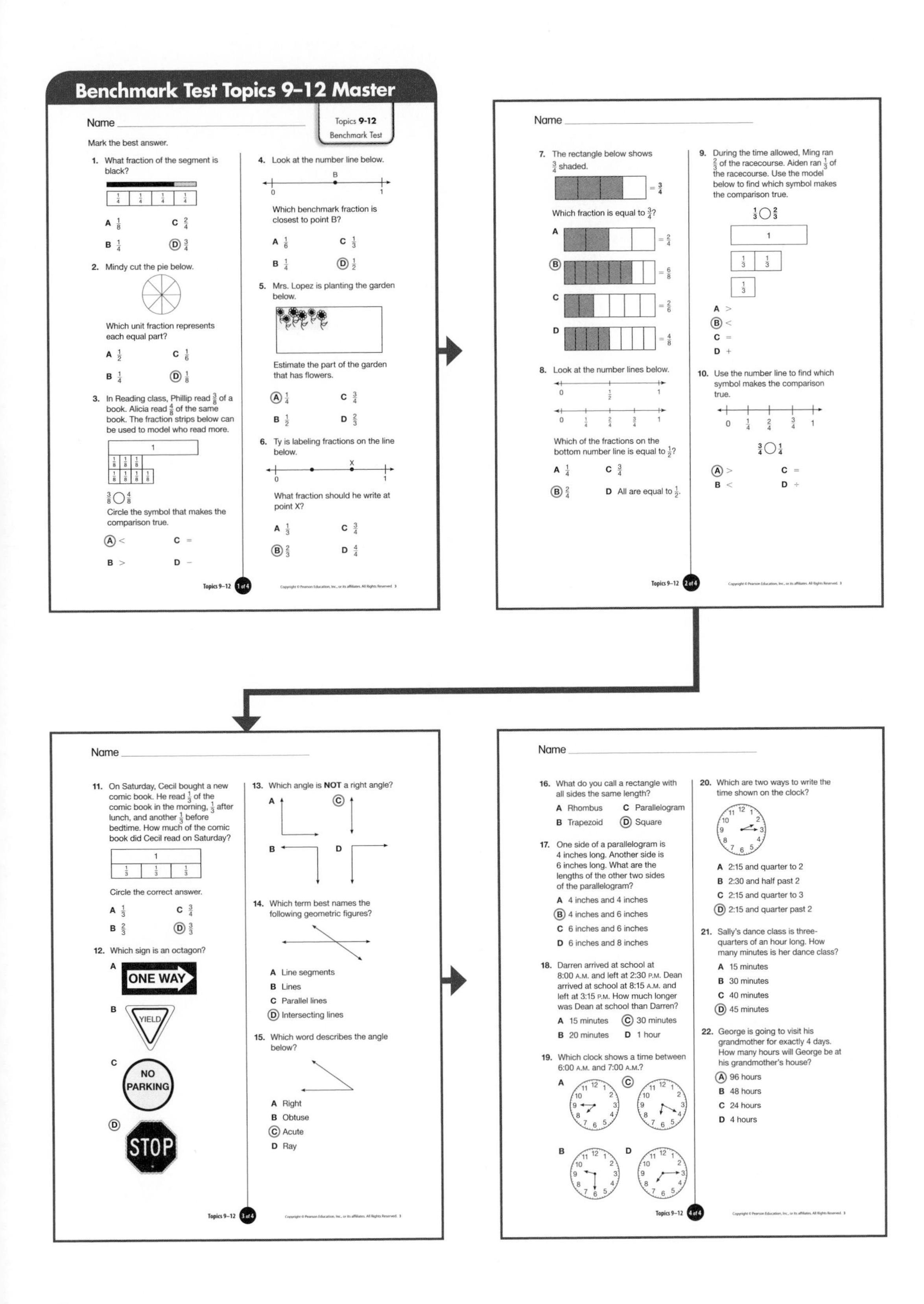
Benchmark Test Topics 9–12 Master

Name ______________ Topics 9–12 Benchmark Test

Mark the best answer.

1. What fraction of the segment is black?
A $\frac{1}{8}$ C $\frac{2}{4}$
B $\frac{1}{4}$ (D) $\frac{3}{4}$

2. Mindy cut the pie below.
Which unit fraction represents each equal part?
A $\frac{1}{2}$ C $\frac{1}{6}$
B $\frac{1}{4}$ (D) $\frac{1}{8}$

3. In Reading class, Phillip read $\frac{3}{8}$ of a book. Alicia read $\frac{4}{8}$ of the same book. The fraction strips below can be used to model who read more.
$\frac{3}{8} \bigcirc \frac{4}{8}$
Circle the symbol that makes the comparison true.
(A) < C =
B > D −

4. Look at the number line below.
Which benchmark fraction is closest to point B?
A $\frac{1}{6}$ C $\frac{1}{3}$
B $\frac{1}{4}$ (D) $\frac{1}{2}$

5. Mrs. Lopez is planting the garden below.
Estimate the part of the garden that has flowers.
(A) $\frac{1}{4}$ C $\frac{3}{4}$
B $\frac{1}{2}$ D $\frac{2}{3}$

6. Ty is labeling fractions on the line below.
What fraction should he write at point X?
A $\frac{1}{3}$ C $\frac{3}{4}$
(B) $\frac{2}{3}$ D $\frac{4}{4}$

Topics 9–12 1 of 4

Name ______________

7. The rectangle below shows $\frac{3}{4}$ shaded.
Which fraction is equal to $\frac{3}{4}$?
A $= \frac{2}{4}$
(B) $= \frac{6}{8}$
C $= \frac{2}{6}$
D $= \frac{4}{8}$

8. Look at the number lines below.
Which of the fractions on the bottom number line is equal to $\frac{1}{2}$?
A $\frac{1}{4}$ C $\frac{3}{4}$
(B) $\frac{2}{4}$ D All are equal to $\frac{1}{2}$.

9. During the time allowed, Ming ran $\frac{2}{3}$ of the racecourse. Aiden ran $\frac{1}{3}$ of the racecourse. Use the model below to find which symbol makes the comparison true.
$\frac{1}{3} \bigcirc \frac{2}{3}$
A >
(B) <
C =
D +

10. Use the number line to find which symbol makes the comparison true.
$\frac{3}{4} \bigcirc \frac{1}{4}$
(A) > C =
B < D ÷

Topics 9–12 2 of 4

Name ______________

11. On Saturday, Cecil bought a new comic book. He read $\frac{1}{3}$ of the comic book in the morning, $\frac{1}{3}$ after lunch, and another $\frac{1}{3}$ before bedtime. How much of the comic book did Cecil read on Saturday?
Circle the correct answer.
A $\frac{1}{3}$ C $\frac{3}{4}$
B $\frac{2}{3}$ (D) $\frac{3}{3}$

12. Which sign is an octagon?
A ONE WAY
B YIELD
C NO PARKING
(D) STOP

13. Which angle is **NOT** a right angle?
A (C)
B D

14. Which term best names the following geometric figures?
A Line segments
B Lines
C Parallel lines
(D) Intersecting lines

15. Which word describes the angle below?
A Right
B Obtuse
(C) Acute
D Ray

Topics 9–12 3 of 4

Name ______________

16. What do you call a rectangle with all sides the same length?
A Rhombus C Parallelogram
B Trapezoid (D) Square

17. One side of a parallelogram is 4 inches long. Another side is 6 inches long. What are the lengths of the other two sides of the parallelogram?
A 4 inches and 4 inches
(B) 4 inches and 6 inches
C 6 inches and 6 inches
D 6 inches and 8 inches

18. Darren arrived at school at 8:00 A.M. and left at 2:30 P.M. Dean arrived at school at 8:15 A.M. and left at 3:15 P.M. How much longer was Dean at school than Darren?
A 15 minutes (C) 30 minutes
B 20 minutes D 1 hour

19. Which clock shows a time between 6:00 A.M. and 7:00 A.M.?
A (C)
B D

20. Which are two ways to write the time shown on the clock?
A 2:15 and quarter to 2
B 2:30 and half past 2
C 2:15 and quarter to 3
(D) 2:15 and quarter past 2

21. Sally's dance class is three-quarters of an hour long. How many minutes is her dance class?
A 15 minutes
B 30 minutes
C 40 minutes
(D) 45 minutes

22. George is going to visit his grandmother for exactly 4 days. How many hours will George be at his grandmother's house?
(A) 96 hours
B 48 hours
C 24 hours
D 4 hours

Topics 9–12 4 of 4

Purpose

- Assess content that is taught in Topics 9–12.